TEACHER EDITION

Carmen Sandiego™ is a trademark of HMH Consumer Company.

Copyright © 2012 by Houghton Mifflin Harcourt Publishing Company.

Common Core State Standards © Copyright 2010. National Governors Association Center for Best Practices and Council of Chief State School Officers. All rights reserved.

This product is not sponsored or endorsed by the Common Core State Standards Initiative of the National Governors Association Center for Best Practices and the Council of Chief State School Officers.

Printed in the U.S.A.

ISBN 978-0-547-59190-2

13 14 0914 20 19 18 17 16 15 14 13

4500429643   C D E F G

 HOUGHTON MIFFLIN HARCOURT

Fluency with Whole Numbers and Decimals

 COMMON CORE

CRITICAL AREA Extending division to 2-digit divisors, integrating decimal fractions into the place value system and developing understanding of operations with decimals to hundredths, and developing fluency with whole number and decimal operations

Domain: **Number and Operations in Base Ten** CC.5.NBT

Lessons	Grade 5 Common Core State Standards
3.1	**Understand the place value system.** **CC.5.NBT.1** Recognize that in a multi-digit number, a digit in one place represents 10 times as much as it represents in the place to its right and 1/10 of what it represents in the place to its left.
3.2	**Understand the place value system.** **CC.5.NBT.3** Read, write, and compare decimals to thousandths. a. Read and write decimals to thousandths using base-ten numerals, number names, and expanded form, e.g., 347.392 = 3 × 100 + 4 × 10 + 7 × 1 + 3 × (1/10) + 9 × (1/100) + 2 × (1/1000).
3.3	**Understand the place value system.** **CC.5.NBT.3** Read, write, and compare decimals to thousandths. b. Compare two decimals to thousandths based on meanings of the digits in each place, using >, =, and < symbols to record the results of comparisons.
3.4	**Understand the place value system.** **CC.5.NBT.4** Use place value understanding to round decimals to any place.
3.5–3.12	**Perform operations with multi-digit whole numbers and with decimals to hundredths.** **CC.5.NBT.7** Add, subtract, multiply, and divide decimals to hundredths, using concrete models or drawings and strategies based on place value, properties of operations, and/or the relationship between addition and subtraction; relate the strategy to a written method and explain the reasoning used.

Table of Contents

Chapter 3 Add and Subtract Decimals

 Domain:
Number and Operations in
Base Ten   **CC.5.NBT**

 Mathematical Practices:

CC.K–12.MP.3 Construct viable arguments and critique the reasoning of others.

CC.K–12.MP.8 Look for and express regularity in repeated reasoning.

Chapter At A Glance

Domain: Number and Operations in Base Ten

Chapter Essential Question How can you add and subtract decimals?

Use the Chapter Planner in the *Go Math! Planning Guide* for pacing.

Lesson At A Glance

	LESSON 3.1 CC.5.NBT.1 Investigate • Thousandths 105A	**LESSON 3.2** CC.5.NBT.3a Place Value of Decimals 109A	**LESSON 3.3** CC.5.NBT.3b Compare and Order Decimals 113A
Essential Question	How can you describe the relationship between two decimal place-value positions?	How do you read, write, and represent decimals through thousandths?	How can you use place value to compare and order decimals?
Objective	Model, read, and write decimals to thousandths.	Read and write decimals through thousandths.	Compare and order decimals to thousandths using place value.
Vocabulary	**thousandth**, hundredth, tenth, place value		
Materials	MathBoard, color pencils, straight edge, 1 per individual, Counting Tape	MathBoard, Counting Tape	MathBoard, Counting Tape

Print Resources

3.1 Student Edition	3.2 Student Edition	3.3 Student Edition
3.1 Standards Practice Book	3.2 Standards Practice Book	3.3 Standards Practice Book
3.1 Reteach	3.2 Reteach	3.3 Reteach
3.1 Enrich	3.2 Enrich	3.3 Enrich
Grab-and-Go™ Centers Kit	Grab-and-Go™ Centers Kit	Grab-and-Go™ Centers Kit
ELL Strategy • Define	**ELL** Strategy • Model Language	**ELL** Strategy • Creative Grouping

Digital Path

3.1 *e*Student Edition	3.2 *e*Student Edition	3.3 *e*Student Edition
3.1 *e*Teacher Edition	3.2 *e*Teacher Edition	3.3 *e*Teacher Edition
Animated Math Models	Animated Math Models	Animated Math Models
	HMH Mega Math	HMH Mega Math

RtI — Response to Intervention

Before the Chapter	During the Lesson	After the Chapter
✓ **Show What You Know**	✓ **Share and Show**	✓ **Chapter Review/Test**
• Prerequisite Skills Activities • Soar to Success Math	• RtI Activities • Mid-Chapter Checkpoint • Soar to Success Math	• RtI Activities • Soar to Success Math

EVERY DAY COUNTS®

Use every day to develop computational fluency.
Visit www.greatsource.com/everydaycounts

Assess Depth of Knowledge

See Chapter 3 Performance Task and
Assessment Guide

LESSON 3.4 CC.5.NBT.4	LESSON 3.5 CC.5.NBT.7	LESSON 3.6 CC.5.NBT.7
Round Decimals 117A	**Investigate • Decimal Addition 121A**	**Investigate • Decimal Subtraction 125A**
How can you use place value to round decimals to a given place?	How can you use base-ten blocks to model decimal addition?	How can you use base-ten blocks to model decimal subtraction?
Round decimals to any place.	Model decimal addition using base-ten blocks.	Model decimal subtraction using base-ten blocks.
round		
MathBoard, Counting Tape	MathBoard, base-ten flats, rods, and units—individual, Counting Tape	MathBoard, base-ten flats, rods, and units—individual, Counting Tape

---

3.4 Student Edition	**3.5 Student Edition**	**3.6 Student Edition**
3.4 Standards Practice Book	**3.5 Standards Practice Book**	**3.6 Standards Practice Book**
3.4 Reteach	3.5 Reteach	3.6 Reteach
3.4 Enrich	3.5 Enrich	3.6 Enrich
Grab-and-Go™ Centers Kit	**Grab-and-Go™ Centers Kit**	**Grab-and-Go™ Centers Kit**
ELL Strategy • Define	**ELL** Strategy • Explore Context	**ELL** Strategy • Describe

---

3.4 *eStudent* Edition	**3.5 *eStudent* Edition**	**3.6 *eStudent* Edition**
3.4 *eTeacher* Edition	**3.5 *eTeacher* Edition**	**3.6 *eTeacher* Edition**
HMH Mega Math		

GREAT ON INTERACTIVE WHITEBOARD!

Digital Path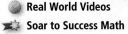

- ☑ **Animated Math Models**
- ✓ **Assessment**
- 🎩 **CARMEN SANDIEGO™**
- 🐾 **HMH Mega Math**
- *iT* **iTools**
- 🆎 **Multimedia *eGlossary***
- 📱 **Professional Development Video Podcasts**
- ⚪ **Real World Videos**
- ⭐ **Soar to Success Math**

Chapter At A Glance

Domain: **Number and Operations in Base Ten**

Lesson At A Glance	LESSON 3.7 CC.5.NBT.7 Estimate Decimal Sums and Differences 131A	LESSON 3.8 CC.5.NBT.7 Add Decimals 135A	LESSON 3.9 CC.5.NBT.7 Subtract Decimals 139A
Essential Question	How can you estimate decimal sums and differences?	How can place value help you add decimals?	How can place value help you subtract decimals?
Objective	Make reasonable estimates of decimal sums and differences.	Add decimals using place value.	Subtract decimals using place value.
Vocabulary	benchmark		
Materials	MathBoard, Counting Tape	MathBoard, Counting Tape	MathBoard, Counting Tape

Print Resources

3.7 Student Edition	**3.8 Student Edition**	**3.9 Student Edition**
3.7 Standards Practice Book	**3.8 Standards Practice Book**	**3.9 Standards Practice Book**
3.7 Reteach	3.8 Reteach	3.9 Reteach
3.7 Enrich	3.8 Enrich	3.9 Enrich
Grab-and-Go™ Centers Kit	**Grab-and-Go™ Centers Kit**	**Grab-and-Go™ Centers Kit**
ELL Strategy • Model Language	**ELL** Strategy • Model Concepts	**ELL** Strategy • Creative Grouping

Digital Path

3.7 *eStudent* Edition	**3.8 *eStudent* Edition**	**3.9 *eStudent* Edition**
3.7 *eTeacher* Edition	**3.8 *eTeacher* Edition**	**3.9 *eTeacher* Edition**
Animated Math Models	**HMH Mega Math**	**Animated Math Models**

Assessment

Diagnostic	Formative	Summative
• **Show What You Know** • **Diagnostic Interview Task** • **Soar to Success Math**	• **Lesson Quick Check** • **Mid-Chapter Checkpoint**	• **Chapter Review/Test** • **Performance Assessment** • **Chapter Test** • **Online Assessment**

LESSON 3.10 CC.5.NBT.7

Algebra • Patterns with Decimals 143A

How can you use addition or subtraction to describe a pattern or create a sequence with decimals?

Identify, describe, and create numeric patterns with decimals.

sequence, **term**

MathBoard, Counting Tape

3.10 Student Edition
3.10 Standards Practice Book
3.10 Reteach
3.10 Enrich
Grab-and-Go™ Centers Kit
ELL Strategy • Model Concepts

3.10 *e*Student Edition
3.10 *e*Teacher Edition
Animated Math Models

LESSON 3.11 CC.5.NBT.7

Problem Solving • Add and Subtract Money 147A

How can the strategy *make a table* help you organize and keep track of your bank account balance?

Solve problems using the strategy *make a table*.

MathBoard, Counting Tape

3.11 Student Edition
3.11 Standards Practice Book
3.11 Reteach
3.11 Enrich
Grab-and-Go™ Centers Kit
ELL Strategy • Model Concepts

3.11 *e*Student Edition
3.11 *e*Teacher Edition
Real World Video, Ch. 3
Animated Math Models
*i*T *i*Tools
HMH Mega Math

LESSON 3.12 CC.5.NBT.7

Choose a Method 151A

Which method could you choose to find decimal sums and differences?

Choose a method to find a decimal sum or difference.

MathBoard, Counting Tape

3.12 Student Edition
3.12 Standards Practice Book
3.12 Reteach
3.12 Enrich
Grab-and-Go™ Centers Kit
ELL Strategy • Identify Relationships

3.12 *e*Student Edition
3.12 *e*Teacher Edition
✓ Chapter 3 Test
Animated Math Models

PROFESSIONAL DEVELOPMENT (COMMON CORE)

Teaching for Depth

by Juli K. Dixon
Professor of Mathematics Education
University of Central Florida
Orlando, Florida

Add Decimals

Modeling decimal addition and subtraction with base-ten blocks provides a method that helps students avoid a common error—operating with decimals as though they are whole numbers, ignoring the significance of the decimal point.

- Students can use base-ten blocks to model decimals. If the flat represents 1, then the long is 0.1 and the small cube is 0.01.

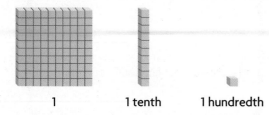

| 1 | 1 tenth | 1 hundredth |

- Using models that represent the process of adding decimals helps students focus on place value.

- This model shows $0.25 + 0.4$. When students use models like this, they see that they are grouping tenths with tenths.

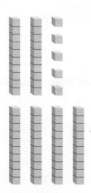

From the Research

"Tell students to 'line up place values' when they compute with decimals. Do not tell them to 'line up decimal points' - that is just a result of lining up place values."
(Ashlock, 2010, p. 86)

Subtract Decimals

Base-ten blocks can help students make sense of regrouping in subtraction of decimals.

- When following the common algorithm to find $3.4 - 1.62$, the problem is rewritten as $3.40 - 1.62$.

- Students who do not have a conceptual understanding of decimals perform the steps by rote and fail to understand that 3.4 is equivalent to 3.40.

- To help students develop their conceptual understanding, have them use models to explore subtraction with decimals (Heddens & Speer, 2006).

COMMON CORE

Mathematical Practices

Students add and subtract decimals using several models. Of particular importance is the place-value model represented with base-ten blocks. As students solve addition problems with base-ten blocks where the flat is equal to one, the long is equal to one-tenth and the small cube is equal to one-hundredth, they are led to see that when adding decimals, the hundredths can be combined with hundredths, the tenths with tenths, and so on. They see that similar reasoning can be applied to subtraction. These experiences help students to **look for and make use of structure** as they make sense of place-value algorithms for adding and subtracting decimals.

PODCASTING

Professional Development Video Podcasts
Place Value and Operations: Decimals, Grades 3–6, Segments 1, 2 and 3

Daily Classroom Management

Differentiated Instruction

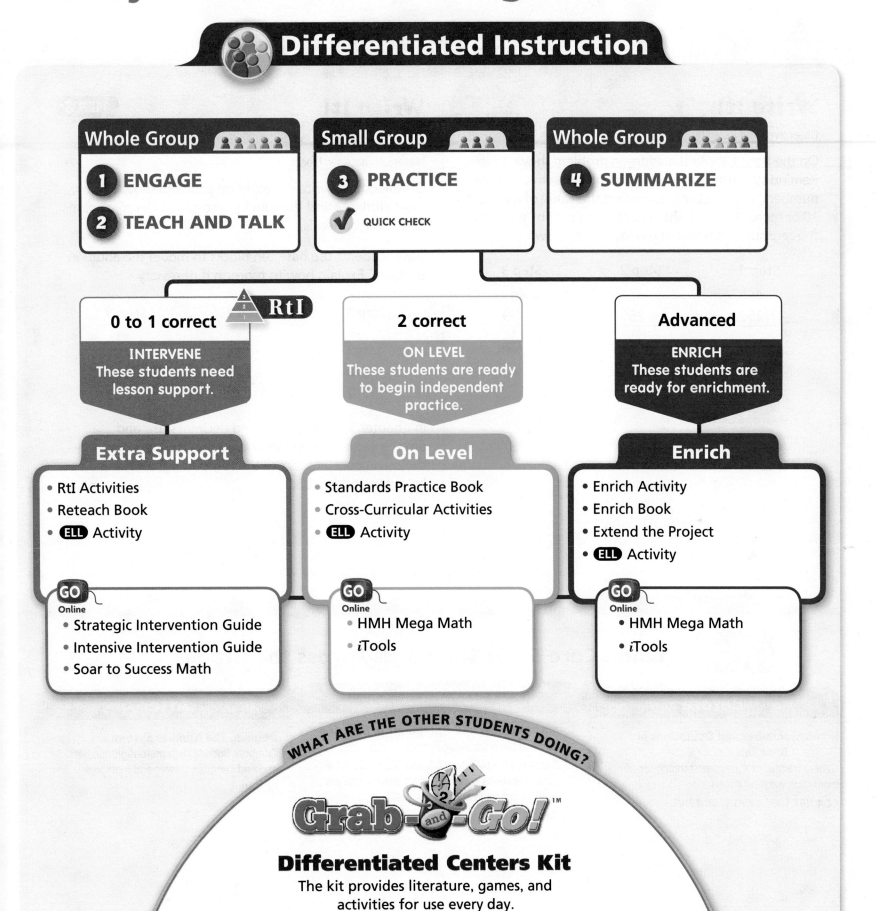

Whole Group

1 ENGAGE

2 TEACH AND TALK

Small Group

3 PRACTICE

✓ QUICK CHECK

Whole Group

4 SUMMARIZE

RtI

0 to 1 correct

INTERVENE
These students need lesson support.

Extra Support

• RtI Activities
• Reteach Book
• ELL Activity

GO Online
• Strategic Intervention Guide
• Intensive Intervention Guide
• Soar to Success Math

---

2 correct

ON LEVEL
These students are ready to begin independent practice.

On Level

• Standards Practice Book
• Cross-Curricular Activities
• ELL Activity

GO Online
• HMH Mega Math
• iTools

Advanced

ENRICH
These students are ready for enrichment.

Enrich

• Enrich Activity
• Enrich Book
• Extend the Project
• ELL Activity

GO Online
• HMH Mega Math
• iTools

WHAT ARE THE OTHER STUDENTS DOING?

Grab-and-Go!™

Differentiated Centers Kit
The kit provides literature, games, and activities for use every day.

Review Prerequisite Skills

 **Activities**

Write It! TIER 2

Objective Find a sum by regrouping below the addends.

On the board, write the addition problem shown below. Remind students that when you find the sum of whole numbers, you must regroup when the value of a place is 10 or more. Then ask them to find the sum by recording the regroupings *below* the addends, as shown.

Step 1	Step 2	Step 3
467	467	467
+ 259	+ 259	+ 259
1	11	11
6	26	726

Write It! TIER 3

Objective Find a sum by regrouping above the addends.

Materials base-ten blocks

On the board, write the addition problem shown below. Have students find the sum by recording the regroupings above the addends.

Have students use base-ten blocks to model the addition problem. Explain how to regroup if necessary.

Step 1	Step 2	Step 3
1	11	11
154	154	154
+ 678	+ 678	+ 678
2	32	832

In Chapter 3, students will find decimal sums and differences, and when their work involves regrouping, they can choose to record the regroupings above or below the addends.

 ## Common Core State Standards Across the Grades

Before	Grade 5	After
Domain: Number and Operations in Base Ten Generalize place value understanding for multi-digit whole numbers. **CC.4.NBT.1, CC.4.NBT.2, CC.4.NBT.3**	**Domain: Number and Operations in Base Ten** Understand the place value system. **CC.5.NBT.1, CC.5.NBT.3a, CC.5.NBT.3b, CC.5.NBT.4** Perform operations with multi-digit whole numbers and with decimals to hundredths. **CC.5.NBT.7**	**Domain: The Number System** Compute fluently with multi-digit numbers and find common factors and multiples. **CC.6.NS.3**

See A page of each lesson for Common Core Standard text.

Developing Math Language

Chapter Vocabulary

sequence an ordered list of numbers

term each of the numbers in a sequence

thousandth one of one thousand equal parts

benchmark a familiar number used as a point of reference

estimate to find a number that is close to an exact amount

hundredth one of one hundred equal parts

round to replace a number with one that is simpler and is approximately the same size as the original number

tenth one of ten equal parts

 **GO Online** Multimedia eGlossary

ELL Vocabulary Activity

Objective Understand the words *overestimate* and *underestimate*.

Materials cards with the words *overestimate* and *underestimate*

Show students a problem such as 34 + 41. Show them how to round both numbers to the nearest ten. Draw an up arrow ↑ beside a number if you round up and a down arrow ↓ beside a number if you round down.

Estimate the sum by adding the rounded numbers.

Ask students if the estimate is an *overestimate* or an *underestimate*.

Practice vocabulary by using questioning strategies such as:

Beginning
- Use your hand to show me *over*. Use your hand to show me *under*.

Intermediate
- If you round both numbers down, will you get an overestimate or an underestimate?

Advanced
- If you round one number up and one number down, how do you know if the estimate is an overestimate or an underestimate?

See **ELL** Activity Guide for leveled activities.

Vocabulary Strategy • Graphic Organizer

Materials Branching Diagram (see *eTeacher Resources*)

Have students complete the branching diagram to brainstorm words that they associate with overestimation and underestimation. Begin with only the word *estimate*. Students fill in the words *overestimate* and *underestimate* in the first two boxes, then words such as *too much*, *more than*, *less than*, *not enough*, etc., to emphasize the meanings of these vocabulary words.

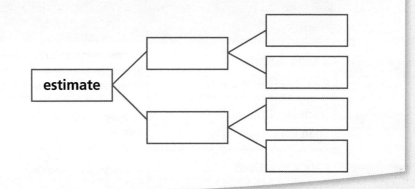

Introduce the Chapter
Assessing Prior Knowledge

Use **Show What You Know** to determine if students need intensive or strategic intervention.

Understanding place value is the key to solving this number logic problem.

Ask:

- **What places are in the number?** tens, ones, tenths, and hundredths **Where will the decimal point go?** after the ones

- **What digit can you place first?** the 8 in the tens place

- **In what place does the digit 2 go?** in the tenths place **Why?** Possible answer: The number in the tenths place is the least digit

- **Where do the last two digits go?** The digit 3 is in the hundredths place and the digit 6 is in the ones place.

 CARMEN SANDIEGO™
Math Detective Activities

Show What You Know ✓

Check your understanding of important skills.

Name _____

▶ **2-Digit Addition and Subtraction** Find the sum or difference.

1.

Hundreds	Tens	Ones
1	1	
	5	8
+	7	6
1	3	4

2.

Hundreds	Tens	Ones
	7	12
	8̸	2̸
−	4	7
	3	5

▶ **Decimals Greater Than One** Write the word form and the expanded form for each.

3. 3.4

three and four tenths

3 + 0.4

4. 2.51

two and fifty-one hundredths

2 + 0.5 + 0.01

▶ **Relate Fractions and Decimals** Write as a decimal or a fraction.

5. 0.8 $\frac{8}{10}$

6. $\frac{5}{100}$ 0.05

7. 0.46 $\frac{46}{100}$

8. $\frac{6}{10}$ 0.6

9. 0.90 $\frac{90}{100}$ or $\frac{9}{10}$

10. $\frac{35}{100}$ 0.35

Jason has 4 tiles. Each tile has a number printed on it. The numbers are 2, 3, 6, and 8. A decimal number is formed using the tiles and the clues. Be a Math Detective and find the number. 86.23

Clues
- The digit in the tens place is the greatest number.
- The digit in the tenths place is less than the digit in the hundredths place.
- The digit in the ones place is greater than the digit in the hundredths place.

GO Online Assessment Options: Soar to Success Math

✔ Show What You Know • Diagnostic Assessment

Use to determine if students need intervention for the chapter's prerequisite skills.

| If NO...then INTERVENE | If YES...then use INDEPENDENT ACTIVITIES |

Were students successful with Show What You Know?

	Skill	Missed More Than	Intervene With	Soar to Success Math
TIER 3	2-Digit Addition and Subtraction	0	*Intensive Intervention* Skill 8; *Intensive Intervention User Guide* Activity 3	Warm-Up 10.34 Warm-Up 11.21
TIER 2	Decimals Greater Than One	0	*Strategic Intervention* Skill 9	Warm-Up 4.25
TIER 2	Relate Fractions and Decimals	2	*Strategic Intervention* Skill 20	Warm-Up 26.35 Warm-Up 26.36

Differentiated Centers Kit

Use the *Enrich Book* or the independent activities in the *Grab-and-Go™ Differentiated Centers Kit*.

For Diagnostic Interview Tasks for Show What You Know skills, see *Assessment Guide*.

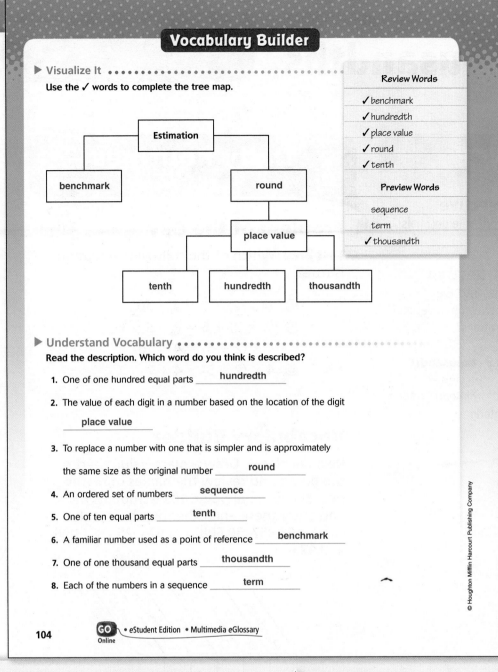

Vocabulary Builder

► Visualize It

Use the ✓ words to complete the tree map.

Estimation
- benchmark
- round
  - place value
    - tenth
    - hundredth
    - thousandth

Review Words
- ✓ benchmark
- ✓ hundredth
- ✓ place value
- ✓ round
- ✓ tenth

Preview Words
- sequence
- term
- ✓ thousandth

► Understand Vocabulary

Read the description. Which word do you think is described?

1. One of one hundred equal parts ___hundredth___

2. The value of each digit in a number based on the location of the digit
   ___place value___

3. To replace a number with one that is simpler and is approximately the same size as the original number ___round___

4. An ordered set of numbers ___sequence___

5. One of ten equal parts ___tenth___

6. A familiar number used as a point of reference ___benchmark___

7. One of one thousand equal parts ___thousandth___

8. Each of the numbers in a sequence ___term___

 • eStudent Edition • Multimedia eGlossary

© Houghton Mifflin Harcourt Publishing Company

Vocabulary Builder MATHEMATICAL PRACTICES

Have students complete the activities on this page by working alone or with partners.

► Visualize It

A tree map helps classify words. Students should use the review words and preview words to complete the tree map.

► Understand Vocabulary

Introduce the words for the chapter.

1. One of one hundred equal parts is a **hundredth**.

2. The value of each digit in a number based on the location of the digit is its **place value**.

3. To replace a number with one that is simpler and is approximately the same size as the original number is to **round**.

4. A **sequence** is an ordered set of numbers.

5. One of ten equal parts is a **tenth**.

6. A **benchmark** is a familiar number used as a point of reference.

7. One of one thousand equal parts is a **thousandth**.

8. Each of the numbers in a sequence is a **term**.

 School-Home Letter available in English and Spanish, *Standards Practice Book*, pp. P51–P52

Intervention Options ▲ RtI Response to Intervention

Use Show What You Know, Lesson Quick Check, and Assessments to diagnose students' intervention levels.

TIER 1	TIER 2	TIER 3	ENRICHMENT
On-Level Intervention	**Strategic Intervention**	**Intensive Intervention**	**Independent Activities**
For students who are generally at grade level but need early intervention with the lesson concepts, use:	For students who need small group instruction to review concepts and skills needed for the chapter, use:	For students who need one-on-one instruction to build foundational skills for the chapter, use:	For students who successfully complete lessons, use:
▲ Tier 1 Activity for every lesson	▲ Tier 2 Activity for every lesson	GO Online Intensive Intervention Guide	Grab-and-Go!™
⭐ Soar to Success Math	GO Online Strategic Intervention Guide	▲ Prerequisite Skills Activities	**Differentiated Centers Kit**
	▲ Prerequisite Skills Activities	⭐ Soar to Success Math	• Enrich Activity for every lesson
	⭐ Soar to Success Math		• Enrich Book
			MM HMH Mega Math

Investigate • Thousandths

LESSON AT A GLANCE

Common Core Standard
Understand the place value system.
CC.5.NBT.1 Recognize that in a multi-digit number, a digit in one place represents 10 times as much as it represents in the place to its right and 1/10 of what it represents in the place to its left.

Also CC.5.NBT.3a

Lesson Objective
Model, read, and write decimals to thousandths.

Essential Question
How can you describe the relationship between two decimal place-value positions?

Vocabulary thousandth

Materials MathBoard, color pencils, straightedge

Digital Path

 Animated Math Models   eStudent Edition

COMMON CORE PROFESSIONAL DEVELOPMENT

About the Math

Teaching for Depth As students extend their understanding of decimal place value to thousandths, take time to relate the decimal places of tenths, hundredths, and thousandths to the base-ten system. Guide students to understand that place values change in the same ways on both sides of the decimal point—that each place has a value 10 times that of the place to its right, and conversely, that each place has a value $\frac{1}{10}$ that of the place to its left. Explain that the thousandths place is not the last place to the right of the decimal point. The places continue to extend to the right, as well as to the left of the decimal point.

Draw a blank place-value chart on the board and have students name and label the places. Then discuss any patterns students notice in the values and the names of the three places to the right and left of the decimal point.

 Professional Development Video Podcasts

Daily Routines Math Board

Common Core

SPIRAL REVIEW

Problem of the Day   eTransparency 3.1

Test Prep Which of the following equations is true?

- Ⓐ $(4 \times 2) + 5 = 4 + 10$
- ⬤ $(4 \times 2) + 5 = 8 + 5$
- Ⓒ $4 \times (2 + 5) = 4 \times 10$
- Ⓓ $4 \times (2 + 5) = 4 + 7$

Vocabulary Builder

Decimal Places Draw a place-value chart on the board and review the names of places near the decimal point. Have students name and enter these and other numbers in the chart: 103.357, 30.608, 135.078, 25.78, 1.006, and 97.603.

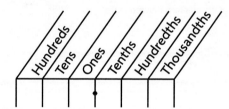

To strengthen understanding of the base-ten nature of these numbers, have students write these numbers in expanded form. Possible example: 97.603 = 9 tens + 7 ones + 6 tenths + 3 thousandths

Differentiated Instruction Activities

ELL Language Support Linguistic | Small Group

Strategy: Define

- Help students understand the differences between the words *tens/tenths, hundreds/hundredths,* and *thousands/thousandths.*

- Write each pair of words on the board. Underline the letters *th.* Then read each pair aloud, emphasizing the difference in pronunciation.

1 thousand = 1,000	1 thousandth = $\frac{1}{1,000}$
1 hundred = 100	1 hundredth = $\frac{1}{100}$
1 ten = 10	1 tenth = $\frac{1}{10}$

- Define the words by saying that *tens, hundreds,* and *thousands* name whole numbers. Add that *tenths, hundredths,* and *thousandths* name parts of a whole.

See **ELL** Activity Guide for leveled activities.

Enrich Logical / Mathematical | Individual

- Explain that the molecular weight of a compound is found by adding the atomic weights of the elements in the compound. Have students use the table below to find the molecular weights of these compounds: NaCl (sodium chloride), KCl (potassium chloride), NaOH (sodium hydroxide), and KOH (potassium hydroxide). NaCl: 58.443; KCl: 74.551; NaOH: 39.997; KOH: 56.105

Element	Symbol	Atomic Weight
Chlorine	Cl	35.453
Hydrogen	H	1.008
Oxygen	O	15.999
Potassium	K	39.098
Sodium	Na	22.99

RtI Response to Intervention

Reteach Tier 1 Visual / Verbal | Whole Class / Small Group

Materials Place-Value Charts (see *eTeacher Resources*)

- Draw a place-value chart on the board.

Ones	Tenths	Hundredths	Thousandths
5	5	0	3

- **In 5.503, what is the value of the first 5?** 5 ones Have a student write the 5 in the correct place in the chart. Continue until the values of all digits have been identified and placed in the chart.

- **Compare the value of the 5 in the ones place to the value of the 5 in the tenths place.** 5 ones is ten times as much as 5 tenths.

- Discuss how the value of the 5 tenths is $\frac{1}{10}$ of 5 ones because of the place-value position each digit occupies.

Tier 2 Visual / Kinesthetic | Small Group

Materials base-ten blocks

- **Show students a big cube and tell them that it equals 1.** Have students pick up their flats. **A flat is $\frac{1}{10}$ of the big cube. What decimal does one flat represent?** Possible answers: Since a flat is one-tenth of a big cube, a flat represents 0.1.

- Have students pick up 1 long. **What part of the big cube is a long? What decimal would one long represent?** Possible answer: A long is $\frac{1}{100}$ of a big cube, so a long equals 0.01.

- Have students pick up their small cubes. **What part of the big cube is a small cube? What decimal would one small cube represent?** Possible answer: A small cube is $\frac{1}{1,000}$ of a big cube, so a small cube equals 0.001.

1 ENGAGE

Materials grid paper

Access Prior Knowledge Have students outline several 10 × 10 squares on grid paper. As you name fractions with denominators of ten or one hundred, have different volunteers shade the grids and share them with the class. Then have students write the shaded part as a fraction and as a decimal.

Use these fractions:

- 6 tenths
- 25 hundredths
- 2 tenths
- 50 hundredths

2 TEACH and TALK GO Online Animated Math Models

▶ Investigate MATHEMATICAL PRACTICES

- **Why is a 10 × 10 grid a good model to represent decimals?** It has 100 squares, so it can be used to represent tenths and hundredths.

After students work through the questions on the student page, ask questions about how tenths, hundredths, and thousandths are related to each other.

- **What is the relationship between one and one tenth?** When one is divided into 10 equal parts, one tenth is one of those parts.

- **What is the relationship between one tenth and one hundredth?** When one tenth is divided into 10 equal parts, one hundredth is one of those parts.

- **What is the relationship between one hundredth and one thousandth?** When one hundredth is divided into 10 equal parts, one thousandth is one of those parts.

Use Math Talk to focus on students' understanding of the model.

MATHEMATICAL PRACTICES Can you name the decimal closest to one? Explain.

 CC.5.NBT.1 Recognize that in a multi-digit number, a digit in one place represents 10 times as much as it represents in the place to its right and 1/10 of what it represents in the place to its left.

Name _____

Thousandths

Essential Question How can you describe the relationship between two decimal place-value positions?

Lesson **3.1**

COMMON CORE STANDARD **CC.5.NBT.1**
Understand the place value system.

Investigate

Materials ■ color pencils ■ straightedge

Thousandths are smaller parts than hundredths. If one hundredth is divided into ten equal parts, each part is one **thousandth**.

Use the model at the right to show tenths, hundredths, and thousandths.

A. Divide the larger square into 10 equal columns or rectangles. Shade one rectangle. What part of the whole is the shaded rectangle? Write that part as a decimal and a fraction.

$0.1; \frac{1}{10}$

B. Divide each rectangle into 10 equal squares. Use a second color to shade in one of the squares. What part of the whole is the shaded square? Write that part as a decimal and a fraction.

$0.01; \frac{1}{100}$

C. Divide the enlarged hundredths square into 10 equal columns or rectangles. If each hundredths square is divided into ten equal rectangles, how many parts will the model have?

1,000 parts

Use a third color to shade one rectangle of the enlarged hundredths square. What part of the whole is the shaded rectangle? Write that part as a decimal and a fraction.

$0.001; \frac{1}{1,000}$

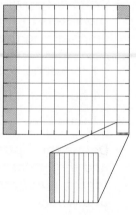

Possible explanation: There are 10 parts when the model is divided into tenths. When the model is divided into hundredths, the 10 parts are each divided into 10 more equal parts; 10 × 10 = 100.

Math Talk MATHEMATICAL PRACTICES
There are 10 times as many hundredths as there are tenths. **Explain** how the model shows this.

© Houghton Mifflin Harcourt Publishing Company

Chapter 3 **105**

Standards Practice 3.1 Common Core SPIRAL REVIEW

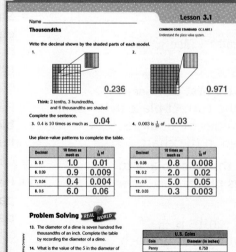

Name _____

Lesson **3.1**

Thousandths

COMMON CORE STANDARD **CC.5.NBT.1**
Understand the place value system.

Write the decimal shown by the shaded parts of each model.

1. **0.236**
2. **0.971**

Think: 2 tenths, 3 thousandths, and 6 thousandths are shaded

Complete the sentence.

3. 0.4 is 10 times as much as **0.04**
4. 0.003 is $\frac{1}{10}$ of **0.03**

Use place-value patterns to complete the table.

Decimal	10 times as much as	$\frac{1}{10}$ of
5. 0.1	1.0	0.01
6. 0.09	0.9	0.009
7. 0.04	0.4	0.004
8. 0.6	6.0	0.06

Decimal	10 times as much as	$\frac{1}{10}$ of
9. 0.08	0.8	0.008
10. 0.2	2.0	0.02
11. 0.5	5.0	0.05
12. 0.03	0.3	0.003

Problem Solving REAL WORLD

13. The diameter of a dime is seven hundred five thousandths of an inch. Complete the table by recording the diameter of a dime.

14. What is the value of the 5 in the diameter of a half dollar?

5 thousandths, or 0.005

15. Which coins have a diameter with a 5 in the hundredths place?

penny and quarter

U.S. Coins

Coin	Diameter (in inches)
Penny	0.750
Nickel	0.835
Dime	0.705
Quarter	0.955
Half dollar	1.205

© Houghton Mifflin Harcourt Publishing Company

Chapter 3 **P53**

Lesson Check (CC.5.NBT.1)

1. What is the relationship between 3.0 and 0.3?
   - (A) 0.3 is 10 times as much as 3.0
   - (B) 3.0 is $\frac{1}{10}$ of 0.3
   - (C) 3.0 is equal to 0.3
   - (●) 0.3 is $\frac{1}{10}$ of 3.0

2. A penny is 0.061 inch thick. What is the value of the 6 in the thickness of a penny?
   - (A) 6 tens
   - (B) 6 thousandths
   - (●) 6 tenths
   - (D) 6 hundredths

Spiral Review (CC.5.OA.1, CC.5.OA.2, CC.5.NBT.1)

3. What is the number seven hundred thirty-one million, nine hundred thirty-four thousand, thirty written in standard form? (Lesson 1.2)
   - (A) 731,934
   - (B) 731,934,003
   - (●) 731,934,030
   - (D) 731,934,300

4. A city has a population of 743,182 people. What is the value of the digit 3? (Lesson 1.2)
   - (A) 3 hundreds
   - (●) 3 thousands
   - (C) 3 ten thousands
   - (D) 3 thousandths

5. Which expression matches the words "three times the sum of 8 and 4"? (Lesson 1.10)
   - (●) 3 × (8 + 4)
   - (B) 3 × 8 + 4
   - (C) 3 + 8 × 4
   - (D) 3 × (8 × 4)

6. A family of 2 adults and 3 children goes to a play. Admission costs $8 per adult and $5 per child. Which expression does NOT show the total admission cost for the family? (Lesson 1.12)
   - (A) ($8 × 2) + ($5 × 3)
   - (B) $16 + $15
   - (●) ($8 × $5) + (2 + 3)
   - (D) $31

© Houghton Mifflin Harcourt Publishing Company

P54

Draw Conclusions

1. **Explain** what each shaded part of your model in the Investigate section shows. What fraction can you write that relates each shaded part to the next greater shaded part? **Possible explanation:** The model shows one tenth, one hundredth, and one thousandth shaded. Each shaded part is $\frac{1}{10}$ of the next larger shaded part.

2. **Identify** and describe a part of your model that shows one thousandth. **Explain** how you know.

   One shaded rectangle of one hundredth that is divided into 10 equal rectangles shows one thousandth. Possible explanation: If each hundredth was divided into 10 equal parts, I would have 10 × 100, or 1,000 parts. Each of the 1,000 parts is $\frac{1}{1,000}$ of the whole.

Make Connections

The relationship of a digit in different place-value positions is the same with decimals as it is with whole numbers. You can use your understanding of place-value patterns and a place-value chart to write decimals that are 10 times as much as or $\frac{1}{10}$ of any given decimal.

Ones	Tenths	Hundredths	Thousandths
	?	0.04	?

10 times as much $\frac{1}{10}$ of

0.4 is 10 times as much as 0.04.

0.004 is $\frac{1}{10}$ of 0.04.

Use the steps below to complete the table.

STEP 1 Write the given decimal in a place-value chart.

STEP 2 Use the place-value chart to write a decimal that is 10 times as much as the given decimal.

STEP 3 Use the place-value chart to write a decimal that is $\frac{1}{10}$ of the given decimal.

Decimal	10 times as much as	$\frac{1}{10}$ of
0.03	0.3	0.003
0.1	1.0	0.01
0.07	0.7	0.007

Possible description: Each place value is $\frac{1}{10}$ of the place value to its left and 10 times as much as the place value to its right.

Math Talk MATHEMATICAL PRACTICES
Describe the pattern you see when you move one decimal place value to the right and one decimal place value to the left.

© Houghton Mifflin Harcourt Publishing Company

106

▶ Draw Conclusions

Give students the opportunity to share their answers with the class.

Reinforce the concept that as you move from tenths to hundredths to thousandths, the value of each place-value position is $\frac{1}{10}$ the value of the previous position.

▶ Make Connections

Ask students which direction the decimal point was moved to write each new decimal. Explain that one tenth is 10 times as much as one hundredth, and one hundredth is $\frac{1}{10}$ of one tenth. If students need help visualizing this concept, have them refer to their models.

- **How did you write a decimal that was 10 times as much as 0.03?** Possible answer: I moved the decimal place one position to the right.

- **How is finding a decimal that is $\frac{1}{10}$ of a number different from finding one that is 10 times as much as a number?** Possible answer: I can find $\frac{1}{10}$ of a number by moving the decimal 1 place to the left, and 10 times as much as a number by moving the decimal 1 place to the right.

Use **Math Talk** to focus on students' understanding of place-value patterns. Students should recognize that as you move from one decimal place-value position to a lesser decimal place-value position, the number of zeros between the digit and the decimal point increases for each place value you move to the right. The reverse is true when you move from a lesser to a greater decimal.

Reteach 3.1 ▲ RtI

Name _____   Lesson 3.1
Reteach

Thousandths

Thousandths are smaller parts than hundredths. If one hundredth is divided into 10 equal parts, each part is one **thousandth**.

Write the decimal shown by the shaded parts of the model.

One column of the decimal model is shaded. It represents one tenth, or _0.1_.

Two small squares of the hundredths are shaded. They represent two hundredths, or _0.02_.

A one-hundredth square is divided into 10 equal parts, or thousandths. Three columns of the thousandth square are shaded. They represent _0.003_.

So, _0.123_ of the decimal model is shaded.

The relationship of a digit in different place-value positions is the same for decimals as for whole numbers.

Write the decimals in a place-value chart.

Ones	Tenths	Hundredths	Thousandths
0	8		
0		8	
0		0	8

0.08 is $\frac{1}{10}$ of _0.8_
0.08 is 10 times as much as _0.008_

1. Write the decimal shown by the shaded parts of the model.
   _0.182_

Use place-value patterns to complete the table.

Decimal	10 times as much as	$\frac{1}{10}$ of	Decimal	10 times as much as	$\frac{1}{10}$ of
2. 0.1	1.0	0.01	5. 0.02	0.2	0.002
3. 0.03	0.3	0.003	6. 0.4	4.0	0.04
4. 0.5	5.0	0.05	7. 0.06	0.6	0.006

Reteach   R22   Grade 5
© Houghton Mifflin Harcourt Publishing Company

Enrich 3.1

Name _____   Lesson 3.1
Enrich

Decimals on the Number Line

The number line below shows decimal values between 1.0 and 2.0. Which number does point P represent?

1.0 ——— 2.0

Since the distance between 1.0 and 2.0 is divided into 10 equal parts, each part is one-tenth. Start at 1.0 and count up by tenths until you reach point P. Point P is at _1.5_

Use the number line above to write the number for each point.

1. point A _1.1_   2. point B _1.8_

Use the number line below to write the number for each point.

3.5 ——— 3.6

3. point C _3.52_   4. point D _3.57_

Use the number line below to write the number for each point.

4.55 ——— 4.56

5. point E _4.551_   6. point F _4.556_

7. Write Math ➤ Draw a number line from 1.88 to 1.89. Label the number 1.886 as point X. **Explain** your thinking. Check students' number lines. Possible answer: there are 10 equal parts between 1.88 and 1.89, so each part is 0.001. I counted 6 thousandths to label point X at 1.886.

Enrich   E22   Grade 5
© Houghton Mifflin Harcourt Publishing Company

⚠ COMMON ERRORS

Error Students write hundredths instead of thousandths for a shaded region.

Example

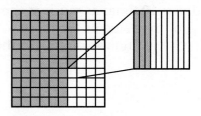

0.69

Springboard to Learning Explain the relationship shown by the model. The model shows 6 tenths + 6 hundredths + 3 thousandths, or 0.663.

3 PRACTICE

▶ Share and Show • Guided Practice

The first problem connects to the learning model. Have students use the MathBoard to explain their thinking.

 Quick Check

If → a student misses Exercises 4 and 6

Then → **Differentiate Instruction** with
- RtI Tier 1 Activity, p. 105B
- Reteach 3.1
- ⭐ Soar to Success Math 4.27

For Exercises 9–16, help students recognize the patterns that occur in the number of zeros between the decimal point and the digit. Have students look at exercises in which a hundredths decimal was given.

- **As you move from the Decimal column to the "10 times as much as" column, what do you notice about the number of zeros between the decimal point and the digit?** The number of zeros decreases.

- **As you move from the Decimal column to the "$\frac{1}{10}$ of" column, what do you notice about the number of zeros between the decimal point and the digit?** The number of zeros increases.

Name _____

Share and Show 🖊️ ....

Write the decimal shown by the shaded parts of each model.

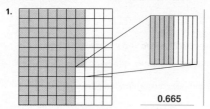

1. 0.665

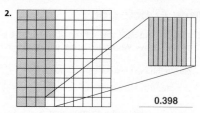

2. 0.398

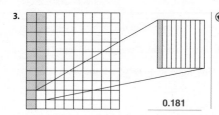

3. 0.181

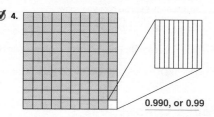

✓ 4. 0.990, or 0.99

Complete the sentence.

5. 0.6 is 10 times as much as __0.06__ .

✓ 6. 0.007 is $\frac{1}{10}$ of __0.07__ .

7. 0.008 is $\frac{1}{10}$ of __0.08__ .

8. 0.5 is 10 times as much as __0.05__ .

Use place-value patterns to complete the table.

	Decimal	10 times as much as	$\frac{1}{10}$ of		Decimal	10 times as much as	$\frac{1}{10}$ of
9.	0.2	2.0	0.02	13.	0.06	0.6	0.006
10.	0.07	0.7	0.007	14.	0.9	9.0	0.09
11.	0.05	0.5	0.005	15.	0.3	3.0	0.03
12.	0.4	4.0	0.04	16.	0.08	0.8	0.008

© Houghton Mifflin Harcourt Publishing Company

Chapter 3 • Lesson 1 **107**

Extend the Math — Activity

Comparing Values

Investigate Students have learned to recognize decimals using place value through the thousandths place. They should understand that the value of one place-value position is 10 times as much as the position to its right and $\frac{1}{10}$ of the value of the place to its left. In this activity, students will find the digit with the appropriate value.

- Write the following numbers on the board: 5,555.55; 22.222.
- Ask volunteers to circle the digit with each of the following values:

  $\frac{1}{10}$ of 2   22.2②2

  10 times as much as 5   5,5⑤5.55

  100 times as much as 5 hundredths   5,55⑤.55

  $\frac{1}{100}$ of 2 tenths   22.22②

Summarize Have students explain how they found the correct digits, and discuss the relationship between place-value positions.

Problem Solving REAL WORLD

Use the table for 17–20.

17. What is the value of the digit 2 in the carpenter bee's length?

2 hundredths, or 0.02

18. If you made a model of a bumblebee that was 10 times as large as the actual bee, how long would the model be in meters? Write your answer as a decimal.

0.19 meter

19. The sweat bee's length is 6 thousandths of a meter. Complete the table by recording the sweat bee's length. **See the table.**

20. H.O.T. An atlas beetle is about 0.14 of a meter long. How does the length of the atlas beetle compare to the length of a leafcutting bee?

The atlas beetle is about 10 times as long

as the leafcutting bee.

21. Write Math ▶ Explain how you can use place value to describe how 0.05 and 0.005 compare.

Possible explanation: Since the digit 5 in 0.05

is one place value to the left of the digit 5 in

0.005, 0.05 is 10 times as much as 0.005 and

0.005 is $\frac{1}{10}$ of 0.05.

22. ⭐ Test Prep What is the relationship between 1.0 and 0.1?

(A) 0.1 is 10 times as much as 1.0

(B) 1.0 is $\frac{1}{10}$ of 0.1

● 0.1 is $\frac{1}{10}$ of 1.0

(D) 1.0 is equal to 0.1

Bee Lengths (in meters)

Bumblebee	0.019
Carpenter Bee	0.025
Leafcutting Bee	0.014
Orchid Bee	0.028
Sweat Bee	0.006

SHOW YOUR WORK

▶ Problem Solving   MATHEMATICAL PRACTICES

H.O.T. Problem Exercise 20 requires students to use reasoning to compare the lengths of insects. Students can write down the values in a place-value chart to help with the comparison.

⭐ Test Prep Coach

Test Prep Coach helps teachers identify common errors that students can make. In Exercise 22, if students selected:

A, B, or **D** They incorrectly identified the relationship between place-value positions.

4 SUMMARIZE   MATHEMATICAL PRACTICES

Essential Question

How can you describe the relationship between two decimal place-value positions?
The value of one place-value position is 10 times as much as the value of the position to its right and $\frac{1}{10}$ of the value of the position to its left.

Math Journal

Write four decimals with the digit 4 in a different place in each—ones, tenths, hundredths, and thousandths. Then write a statement that compares the value of the digit 4 in the different decimals.

Differentiated Instruction — INDEPENDENT ACTIVITIES

Grab-and-Go!
Differentiated Centers Kit

Activities
Do We Decimal?

Students complete orange Activity Card 4 by drawing models of decimals and representing the models as decimals and as fractions.

Literature
Dewey and His Decimals

Students read about the Dewey Decimal system used to order books in the library.

Digital Path

- 📺 Animated Math Models
- *i*T *i*Tools
- MM HMH Mega Math
- ☆ Soar to Success Math
- GO MATH *e*Student Edition

Place Value of Decimals

LESSON AT A GLANCE

Common Core Standard
Understand the place value system.
CC.5.NBT.3a Read, write, and compare decimals to thousandths. Read and write decimals to thousandths using base-ten numerals, number names, and expanded form, e.g., 347.392 = 3 × 100 + 4 × 10 + 7 × 1 + 3 × (1/10) + 9 × (1/100) + 2 × (1/1000).

Also CC.5.NBT.1

Lesson Objective
Read and write decimals through thousandths.

Essential Question
How do you read, write, and represent decimals through thousandths?

Materials
MathBoard

Digital Path

 Animated Math Models   𝖶𝖬 HMH Mega Math

📖 eStudent Edition

COMMON CORE
PROFESSIONAL DEVELOPMENT

About the Math

Why Teach This It is important to have a firm understanding of place value to understand operations with decimals later.

In this lesson, students read and write decimals through thousandths. A place-value chart can help students see the value of each digit and the relationship between the places. Each place value is $\frac{1}{10}$ of the place value that precedes it, and 10 times as much as the place value that follows it. So, one hundredth is $\frac{1}{10}$ of one tenth and 10 times as much as one thousandth.

Students recognize that zeros written at the end of a decimal change how the decimal is read, but do not change its value: 0.5 = 0.50 = 0.500 or 5 tenths = 50 hundredths = 500 thousandths.

 Professional Development Video Podcasts

Daily Routines

Math Board

Common Core

SPIRAL REVIEW

Problem of the Day

eTransparency
3.2

Test Prep Mr. Yandle tracks the number of hits on his company's web site for six months. He finds that there were three hundred sixty-five thousand, seventy-four hits. What is this number in standard form?

   Ⓐ 365 + 74   ● 365,074
   Ⓑ 365,000 + 74   Ⓓ 365,740

Fluency Builder

Materials Spinners (see *eTeacher Resources*)

Adding Whole Numbers Draw the following template on the board:

$$\square\square\square,\square\square\square$$
$$+\ \square\square\square,\square\square\square$$

Have students copy the template on paper. Then have students spin a spinner numbered 0 to 9 and write digits in the template to form two 6-digit numbers. When done, students can find the sum and check their answer with a partner. Have students continue to form new addition problems.

Literature

From the Grab-and-Go™ Differentiated Centers Kit

Students read about the Dewey Decimal system used to order books in the library.

Dewey and His Decimals

Differentiated Instruction Activities

ELL Language Support
 Auditory / Visual
Small Group

Strategy: Model Language

- Reading and writing decimals may be difficult for English learners. Model how to pronounce and write decimals as students work through the lesson.

> 0.253
>
> two hundred fifty-three thousandths

- As students work on standard form, read the numbers slowly. Ask students to repeat what you say. Write the word form and then have students copy it.

- Continue by changing one or two digits in a number. Have students read it and write the word form.

See ELL Activity Guide for leveled activities.

Enrich
 Visual / Kinesthetic
Individual

Materials Place-Value Chart, Spinners (see *eTeacher Resources*)

- Have students spin a spinner labeled from 0 to 9. Students spin four times. After each spin, they can write the digit in either the ones place, the tenths place, the hundredths place, or the thousandths place of a place-value chart.

Ones	Tenths	Hundredths	Thousandths
	•	2	

- After writing the last digit in the place-value chart, have students write the decimal in standard form, word form, and expanded form.

- Students can continue spinning to form new decimals and write them in standard form, word form, and expanded form.

RtI Response to Intervention

Reteach Tier 1
 Visual / Verbal
Whole Class / Small Group

- Draw a place-value chart on the board. Discuss how each place value is $\frac{1}{10}$ of the place value to its left or 10 times as much as the place value to its right. Write 1.269 in the chart.

Tens	Ones	Tenths	Hundredths	Thousandths
	1 •	2	6	9

- **What is the place value of the digit 9?** thousandths

- **What is the value of the digit 9?** 9 thousandths
  Ask what the values of the other digits in the decimal are.

- **What is 1.269 written in expanded form?**
  $1 \times 1 + 2 \times (\frac{1}{10}) + 6 \times (\frac{1}{100}) + 9 \times (\frac{1}{1,000})$

- **What is the word form of the number?**
  one and two hundred sixty-nine thousandths

Tier 2
Visual / Kinesthetic
Small Group

Materials Place-Value Charts (see *eTeacher Resources*)

- Write the number 0.245 on the board.

- Help students write the number in a place-value chart, making sure each digit is placed correctly. Review the value of each digit.

Tens	Ones	Tenths	Hundredths	Thousandths
	0 •	2	4	5

- Explain to students that the value of the place at the farthest right can help name the decimal.

- **Which digit is farthest right?** 5 **What is the place value of the digit 5?** thousandths

- **How can you read the decimal?** two hundred forty-five thousandths

1 ENGAGE

Access Prior Knowledge Introduce the lesson by discussing how measurements are often given using decimals to provide a more precise measurement. Brainstorm examples when decimals are used for measuring. For example, swimming competitions give times using decimals to the hundredths place to determine a winner.

2 TEACH and TALK Animated Math Models

▶ **Unlock the Problem** MATHEMATICAL PRACTICES

Read and discuss the problem. Direct students' attention to the place-value chart.

- **How does each decimal place value compare to the place value to its left?** Each place value is $\frac{1}{10}$ of the place value to its left.

- **How does each decimal place value compare to the place value to its right?** Each place value is 10 times as much as the place value to its right.

- **The last row in the place-value chart shows the value of each digit. What pattern do you notice as you move from one place value to the next lesser place value?** Possible answer: Another zero is written to the right of the decimal point, between the decimal point and the digit.

- **What is the value of the digit 7 in 1.726? How does this relate to the expanded form of 1.726?** The value of the digit 7 is 7 tenths. Possible answer: The expanded form of 1.726 shows the value of the 7 in the tenths place by multiplying 7 by $\frac{1}{10}$.

Use Math Talk to focus on students' understanding of how to read a decimal. Point out to students that the decimal point is written in word form and read as *and*.

Try This!

Students use place value to read and write decimals.

- **For Example B, explain how you can write the standard form of the decimal.** Possible answer: I can read the word form of the decimal. The "and" represents the decimal, so "three and" means "3." Then "thousandths" means that the last digit is in the thousandths place. I can write 614 for "six hundred fourteen" and place the last digit 4 in the thousandths place to get 3.614.

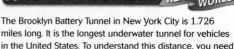

CC.5.NBT.3a Read, write, and compare decimals to thousandths. Read and write decimals to thousandths using base-ten numerals, number names, and expanded form, e.g., 347.392 = 3 × 100 + 4 × 10 + 7 × 1 + 3 × (1/10) + 9 × (1/100) + 2 × (1/1000).

Name _____

Place Value of Decimals

Lesson **3.2**

COMMON CORE STANDARD CC.5.NBT.3a
Understand the place value system.

Essential Question How do you read, write, and represent decimals through thousandths?

🔓 UNLOCK the Problem REAL WORLD

▲ The Brooklyn Battery Tunnel passes under the East River.

The Brooklyn Battery Tunnel in New York City is 1.726 miles long. It is the longest underwater tunnel for vehicles in the United States. To understand this distance, you need to understand the place value of each digit in 1.726.

You can use a place-value chart to understand decimals. Whole numbers are to the left of the decimal point. Decimals are to the right of the decimal point. The thousandths place is to the right of the hundredths place.

Tens	Ones	Tenths	Hundredths	Thousandths
	1 •	7	2	6
1	1×1	$7 \times \frac{1}{10}$	$2 \times \frac{1}{100}$	$6 \times \frac{1}{1,000}$
	1.0	0.7	0.02	0.006

Value

The place value of the digit 6 in 1.726 is thousandths. The value of 6 in 1.726 is $6 \times \frac{1}{1,000}$, or 0.006.

Standard Form: 1.726
Word Form: one and seven hundred twenty-six thousandths

Expanded Form: $1 \times 1 + 7 \times \left(\frac{1}{10}\right) + 2 \times \left(\frac{1}{100}\right) + 6 \times \left(\frac{1}{1,000}\right)$

Possible explanation: The last digit of a decimal determines the name of the decimal, such as tenths, hundredths, and thousandths.

Math Talk MATHEMATICAL PRACTICES
Explain how the value of the last digit in a decimal can help you read a decimal.

Try This! Use place value to read and write decimals.

Ⓐ **Standard Form:** 2.35
Word Form: two and ___thirty-five hundredths___
Expanded Form: $2 \times 1+$ ___$3 \times \left(\frac{1}{10}\right) + 5 \times \left(\frac{1}{100}\right)$___

Ⓑ **Standard Form:** ___3.614___
Word Form: three and six hundred fourteen thousandths
Expanded Form: ___3×1___ $+ 6 \times \left(\frac{1}{10}\right) +$ ___$1 \times \left(\frac{1}{100}\right)$___ $+$ ___$4 \times \left(\frac{1}{1,000}\right)$___

Chapter 3 **109**

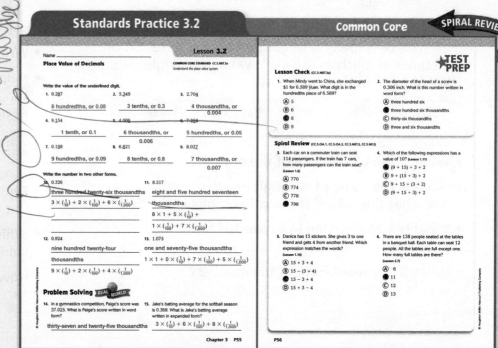

Standards Practice 3.2 **Common Core** SPIRAL REVIEW

Name _____

Place Value of Decimals

Lesson **3.2**

COMMON CORE STANDARD CC.5.NBT.3a
Understand the place value system.

Write the value of the underlined digit.

1. 0.287
8 hundredths, or 0.08

2. 5.3<u>4</u>9
3 tenths, or 0.3

3. 2.70<u>4</u>
4 thousandths, or 0.004

4. 9.1<u>5</u>4
1 tenth, or 0.1

5. 4.00<u>6</u>
6 thousandths, or 0.006

6. 7.2<u>5</u>0
5 hundredths, or 0.05

7. 0.1<u>9</u>8
9 hundredths, or 0.09

8. 6.<u>8</u>21
8 tenths, or 0.8

9. 8.02<u>7</u>
7 thousandths, or 0.007

Write the number in two other forms.

10. 0.326
three hundred twenty-six thousandths
$3 \times \left(\frac{1}{10}\right) + 2 \times \left(\frac{1}{100}\right) + 6 \times \left(\frac{1}{1,000}\right)$

11. 8.517
eight and five hundred seventeen thousandths
$8 \times 1 + 5 \times \left(\frac{1}{10}\right) + 1 \times \left(\frac{1}{100}\right) + 7 \times \left(\frac{1}{1,000}\right)$

12. 0.924
nine hundred twenty-four thousandths
$9 \times \left(\frac{1}{10}\right) + 2 \times \left(\frac{1}{100}\right) + 4 \times \left(\frac{1}{1,000}\right)$

13. 1.075
one and seventy-five thousandths
$1 \times 1 + 0 \times \left(\frac{1}{10}\right) + 7 \times \left(\frac{1}{100}\right) + 5 \times \left(\frac{1}{1,000}\right)$

Problem Solving REAL WORLD

14. In a gymnastics competition, Paige's score was 37.025. What is Paige's score written in word form?
thirty-seven and twenty-five thousandths

15. Jake's batting average for the softball season is 0.368. What is Jake's batting average written in expanded form?
$3 \times \left(\frac{1}{10}\right) + 6 \times \left(\frac{1}{100}\right) + 8 \times \left(\frac{1}{1,000}\right)$

Chapter 3 **PS5**

Lesson Check (CC.5.NBT.3a)

1. When Mindy went to China, she exchanged $1 for 6.589 Yuan. What digit is in the hundredths place of 6.589?
Ⓐ 5
Ⓑ 6
● 8
Ⓓ 9

2. The diameter of the head of a screw is 0.306 inch. What is this number written in word form?
Ⓐ three hundred six
● three hundred six thousandths
Ⓒ thirty-six thousandths
Ⓓ three and six thousandths

Spiral Review (CC.5.OA.1, CC.5.OA.2, CC.5.NBT.5, CC.5.NF.3)

3. Each car on a commuter train can seat 114 passengers. If the train has 7 cars, how many passengers can the train seat? (Lesson 1.6)
Ⓐ 770
Ⓑ 774
Ⓒ 778
● 798

4. Which of the following expressions has a value of 10? (Lesson 1.11)
● (9 + 15) ÷ 3 + 2
Ⓑ 9 + (15 ÷ 3) + 2
Ⓒ 9 ÷ (15 ÷ 3) + 2
Ⓓ (9 + 15 ÷ 3) + 2

5. Danica has 15 stickers. She gives 3 to one friend and gets 4 from another friend. Which expression matches the words? (Lesson 1.10)
Ⓐ 15 ÷ 3 + 4
Ⓑ 15 − (3 + 4)
● 15 − 3 + 4
Ⓓ 15 ÷ 3 − 4

6. There are 138 people seated at the tables in a banquet hall. Each table can seat 12 people. All the tables are full except one. How many full tables are there? (Lesson 2.7)
Ⓐ 6
● 11
Ⓒ 12
Ⓓ 13

P56

Example Use a place-value chart.

The silk spun by a common garden spider is about 0.003 millimeter thick. A commonly used sewing thread is about 0.3 millimeter thick. How does the thickness of the spider silk and the thread compare?

STEP 1 Write the numbers in a place-value chart.

Ones	Tenths	Hundredths	Thousandths
0	3		
0	0	0	3

STEP 2

Count the number of decimal place-value positions to the digit 3 in 0.3 and 0.003.

0.3 has ___2___ fewer decimal places than 0.003

2 fewer decimal places: $10 \times 10 =$ ___100___

0.3 is ___100___ times as much as 0.003

0.003 is $\frac{1}{100}$ of 0.3

So, the thread is ___100___ times as thick as the garden spider's silk. The thickness of the garden spider's silk is $\frac{1}{100}$ that of the thread.

You can use place-value patterns to rename a decimal.

Try This! Use place-value patterns.

Rename 0.3 using other place values.

0.300	3 tenths	$3 \times \frac{1}{10}$
0.300	__30__ hundredths	__30__ $\times \frac{1}{100}$
0.300	**300 thousandths**	$300 \times \frac{1}{1,000}$

110

© Houghton Mifflin Harcourt Publishing Company

Example

Work through the example with students. Be sure students recognize that the value of each place is $\frac{1}{10}$ the value of the place to its left or 10 times as much as the value of the place to its right.

- **How do you know that 0.3 is greater than 0.003?** Possible answer: 0.3 is greater because the value of the digit 3 decreases as I move across the place-value chart from left to right. So, 0.3 is 100 times as much as 0.003.

Try This!

Students should recognize that zeros written at the end of a decimal change the way the decimal is read, but do not change its value.

- **Compare the values of 0.3 and 0.30.** Possible answer: 0.3 is 3 tenths. 0.30 is 30 hundredths, which is the same as 3 tenths.

- **How does writing a zero at the end of a decimal change it?** Possible answer: The value is not changed, just the way you read the decimal.

Go Deeper

- **Explain how to find the unknown factor: 0.035 = 35 × ■.** Possible explanation: I can use the place value of the digit farthest to the right, 5, as the unknown factor, which is 1 thousandth. So, $0.035 = 35 \times \frac{1}{1,000}$.

COMMON ERRORS

Error Students may not write a decimal in word form correctly.

Example In word form, 0.489 is written as four hundred eighty-nine tenths.

Springboard to Learning Have students use a place-value chart to put each digit in its correct place-value position. Then ask students to circle the place value farthest to the right. Tell students to name the decimal using this place value.

③ PRACTICE

▶ Share and Show • Guided Practice

The first problem connects to the learning model. Have students use the MathBoard to explain their thinking.

Use Exercises 4 and 6 for **Quick Check**. Students should show their answers for the Quick Check on the MathBoard.

 Quick Check 🔺 **RtI**

If ➤ a student misses Exercises 4 and 6

Then ➤ **Differentiate Instruction with**
- RtI Tier 1 Activity, p. 109B
- Reteach 3.2
- ⭐ Soar to Success Math 4.27

▶ On Your Own • Independent Practice

If students complete Exercises 4 and 6 correctly, they may continue with Independent Practice. Assign Exercises 7–14.

Name _____

Share and Show ....

1. Complete the place-value chart to find the value of each digit.

Ones	Tenths	Hundredths	Thousandths
3 •	5	2	4
3×1	$5 \times \frac{1}{10}$	$2 \times \frac{1}{100}$	$4 \times \frac{1}{1,000}$	} Value
3	0.5	0.02	0.004

Write the value of the underlined digit.

2. 0.5<u>4</u>3
four hundredths, or 0.04

3. 6.<u>2</u>34
two tenths, or 0.2

✓ **4.** 3.95<u>4</u>
four thousandths, or 0.004

Write the number in two other forms.

5. 0.253
two hundred fifty-three thousandths
$2 \times \left(\frac{1}{10}\right) + 5 \times \left(\frac{1}{100}\right) + 3 \times \left(\frac{1}{1,000}\right)$

✓ **6.** 7.632
seven and six hundred thirty-two thousandths
$7 \times 1 + 6 \times \left(\frac{1}{10}\right) + 3 \times \left(\frac{1}{100}\right) + 2 \times \left(\frac{1}{1,000}\right)$

On Your Own ....

Write the value of the underlined digit.

7. 0.4<u>9</u>6
nine hundredths, or 0.09

8. 2.<u>7</u>26
seven tenths, or 0.7

9. 1.06<u>6</u>
six thousandths, or 0.006

10. 6.<u>3</u>99
three tenths, or 0.3

11. 0.00<u>2</u>
two thousandths, or 0.002

12. 14.37<u>1</u>
one thousandth, or 0.001

Write the number in two other forms.

13. 0.489
four hundred eighty-nine thousandths
$4 \times \left(\frac{1}{10}\right) + 8 \times \left(\frac{1}{100}\right) + 9 \times \left(\frac{1}{1,000}\right)$

14. 5.916
five and nine hundred sixteen thousandths
$5 \times 1 + 9 \times \left(\frac{1}{10}\right) + 1 \times \left(\frac{1}{100}\right) + 6 \times \left(\frac{1}{1,000}\right)$

© Houghton Mifflin Harcourt Publishing Company

Chapter 3 • Lesson 2 111

Cross-Curricular   SCIENCE

- Fossils are the prehistoric remains of plants or animals.
- There are two types of fossils: body fossils or trace fossils. A body fossil has been preserved in mud and sand, tar, lava, or frozen in ice. A trace fossil is a sign of a plant or an animal that has been preserved in rock, such as a leaf imprint or animal footprint.
- Some interesting fossils have been found. For example, geologists found a cockroach that measured 3.453 inches long! What is the number 3.453 written in expanded form?
$3 \times 1 + 4 \times \left(\frac{1}{10}\right) + 5 \times \left(\frac{1}{100}\right) + 3 \times \left(\frac{1}{1,000}\right)$

SOCIAL STUDIES

- Rhode Island was one of the original 13 colonies. It was also the first colony to attack British rule. On May 4, 1776, Rhode Island declared its independence from Great Britain.
- Rhode Island was also the last of the original 13 colonies to ratify the U.S. Constitution, demanding that the Bill of Rights be added.
- Of the 50 states, Rhode Island is the smallest. It ranks last in total land and water area. It has a total area of 1,545.05 square miles. Write 1,545.05 in word form.
one thousand, five hundred forty-five and 5 hundredths

111   Chapter 3

Problem Solving REAL WORLD

Use the table for 15–17.

15. What is the value of the digit 7 in New Mexico's average annual rainfall?

seven hundredths, or 0.07

16. The average annual rainfall in Maine is one and seventy-four thousandths of a meter per year. Complete the table by writing that amount in standard form. **See the table.**

17. Which of the states has an average annual rainfall with the least number in the thousandths place?

Wisconsin

18. **H.O.T.** What's the Error? Damian wrote the number four and twenty-three thousandths as 4.23. Describe and correct his error.

Possible description: Damian did not

include a place holder in the tenths

place; 4.023.

19. **Write Math** Explain how you know that the digit 6 in the numbers 3.675 and 3.756 does not have the same value.

Possible explanation: In 3.675, the digit

6 is in the tenths place, so its value is

$6 \times \frac{1}{10}$, **or 0.6. In 3.756, the digit 6 is in**

the thousandths place, so its value is

$6 \times \frac{1}{1,000}$, **or 0.006.**

20. **Test Prep** In 24.736, which digit is in the thousandths place?
- (A) 3
- (B) 4
- (C) 6
- (D) 7

Average Annual Rainfall (in meters)	
California	0.564
New Mexico	0.372
New York	1.041
Wisconsin	0.820
Maine	**1.074**

SHOW YOUR WORK

112 FOR MORE PRACTICE:
Standards Practice Book, pp. P55–P56

FOR EXTRA PRACTICE:
Standards Practice Book, p. P77

▶ ## Problem Solving

Students gather information from a table to answer Exercises 15–17.

⭐ Test Prep Coach

Test Prep Coach helps teachers to identify common errors that students can make.

In Exercise 20, if students selected:

A, B, or **D** They incorrectly identify the decimal place value.

4 SUMMARIZE MATHEMATICAL PRACTICES

Essential Question

How do you read, write, and represent decimals though thousandths? Possible answer: You can use a place-value chart to help you see the value of each digit. Each place is 10 times as much as the place to its right. A decimal can be written in standard form, word form, or expanded form. The last digit determines the name of the decimal.

Math Journal

Write Standard Form, Expanded Form, and Word Form at the top of a page. Under Standard Form, write five decimals that have at least 3 digits to the right of the decimal point. Write the expanded form and the word form for each number under the appropriate heading.

Differentiated Instruction / INDEPENDENT ACTIVITIES

Differentiated Centers Kit

Activities
Do We Decimal?

Students complete orange Activity Card 4 by drawing models of decimals and representing the models as decimals and as fractions.

Literature
Dewey and His Decimals

Students read about the Dewey Decimal system used to order books in the library.

Digital Path

- 📺 Animated Math Models
- iT iTools
- 🎵 HMH Mega Math
- ⭐ Soar to Success Math
- GO eStudent Edition

Lesson 3.2 112

Compare and Order Decimals

LESSON AT A GLANCE

Common Core Standard
Understand the place value system.
CC.5.NBT.3b Read, write, and compare decimals to thousandths. Compare two decimals to thousandths based on meanings of the digits in each place, using >, =, and < symbols to record the results of comparisons.

Lesson Objective
Compare and order decimals to thousandths using place value.

Essential Question
How can you use place value to compare and order decimals?

Materials
MathBoard

Digital Path

 Animated Math Models    HMH Mega Math

📲 eStudent Edition

COMMON CORE PROFESSIONAL DEVELOPMENT

About the Math

Teaching for Depth Comparing decimals is similar to comparing whole numbers because both compare from left to right, or from greater to lesser place-value positions. A place-value chart helps to line up the decimal points and place-value positions before comparing.

When comparing decimals in a place-value chart, you compare the digits from left to right to compare the greater values first. Students should recognize that the greater place-value position where the digits differ identifies the greater number.

When comparing decimals to order them, you first compare all digits in the greatest place-value position. If all the digits are different, the order of the digits is the order of the numbers. If all the digits are the same, move to the next lesser place-value position and compare the digits. If some digits are different and some are the same, order the digits and then determine the order of the digits that are the same by moving to the next lesser place-value position.

 Professional Development Video Podcasts

Daily Routines 📋 Math Board

Common Core

Problem of the Day

 eTransparency 3.3

Test Prep Max competed in a 50-meter freestyle swimming event. His finishing time was 31.26 seconds. What is the value of the digit 6 in Max's time?

Ⓐ 6 tens   Ⓒ 6 tenths

Ⓑ 6 ones   ● 6 hundredths

Fluency Builder

Counting Tape

Materials Counting Tape

On Day 33 you'll want to have a discussion (similar to Day 25) to show that 33 is about $\frac{1}{3}$ of 100. Students can discuss taking the one leftover hundredth and dividing it among the three groups of thirty-three to end up with $\frac{1}{3}$ = 33 and $\frac{1}{3}$ hundredths, or $33\frac{1}{3}$%.

Questions to encourage decimal number sense might include the following.

- Which is greater, $\frac{1}{4}$ or 0.20? $\frac{1}{4}$
- How much is $\frac{1}{4}$ of a dollar? 25 cents
- If a coat that costs $100 is on sale for 25% off, how much can we take off the price? $25
- Which is greater, $\frac{1}{3}$ or 0.30? Explain. $\frac{1}{3}$
- What is 10% of a dollar? 10 cents
- What is 30% of a dollar? 30 cents
- What is 30% of $2? 60 cents

			0.3						
0.27	0.28	0.29	0.30	0.31	0.32	0.33	0.34	0.35	0.36
			$\frac{3}{10}$			$\frac{1}{3}$			

Differentiated Instruction Activities

ELL Language Support Interpersonal / Social Partners

Strategy: **Creative Grouping**

- Partner advanced English learners or students who are fluent in English with beginning and intermediate students.

- Have students practice comparing decimals. Have the advanced English learners explain the process of comparing decimals first.

- Then have the beginning and intermediate students explain the process either verbally or in drawings.

See **ELL** Activity Guide for leveled activities.

Enrich Visual Partners

Materials index cards

- Give each student 10 index cards, and have them write a decimal up to thousandths on each card.

| 0.782 | 0.669 |

- Have partners combine their cards, shuffle them, and then divide them into two equal piles. Each student takes a pile and keeps the cards facedown.

- Partners turn over their top cards at the same time and compare the decimals. The student with the greater decimal keeps the cards.

- Play continues until one student has all the cards and is declared the winner.

RtI Response to Intervention

Reteach Tier 1 Visual Whole Class / Small Group

- Write the numbers 1.37, 1.703, and 1.307 on the board, aligning the decimal points. Have students order the decimals from least to greatest.

    1.37

    1.703

    1.307

- **Start with the greatest place-value position. Compare the ones.** 1 = 1 = 1

- **The digits are all the same, so compare the digits in the tenths place.** 7 > 3 **Which number is greatest?** 1.703

- **Now compare the remaining two numbers, 1.37 and 1.307. Compare the digits in the hundredths place.** 7 > 0 **Which number is least?** 1.307

- **Now order the numbers from least to greatest.** 1.307, 1.37, 1.703

Tier 2 Visual / Kinesthetic Small Group

Materials Place-Value Charts (see *eTeacher Resources*)

- Write the numbers 1.345 and 1.354 on the board.

Ones	Tenths	Hundredths	Thousandths
1 •	3	4	5
1 •	3	5	4

- Have students start at the greatest place-value position, and compare the digits.

- **Which place-value position is greatest?** ones **Compare the digits.** 1 = 1

- **The digits are the same. Move to the tenths place.** Have students compare the digits. 3 = 3

- **The digits are the same.** Have students compare the digits in the hundredths place. 4 < 5 or 5 > 4

- **Compare the numbers.** 1.345 < 1.354 or 1.354 > 1.345

1 ENGAGE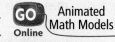

Access Prior Knowledge Write the following numbers on the board: 32,045; 321,459; 32,405. Discuss how to order the whole numbers.

- **How can you order these numbers from least to greatest?** 32,045; 32,405; 321,459; Possible explanation: I compare the digits in the same place-value position, moving from left to right and starting from the greatest place value.

2 TEACH and TALK Animated Math Models

▶ Unlock the Problem 🔷 MATHEMATICAL PRACTICES

Read and discuss the problem.

- **What are you comparing?** the height of Cloud Mountain, 2.495 miles, and the height of Boundary Mountain, 2.488 miles

▶ One Way

Discuss how to line up place values and compare the digits from left to right.

- **What happens if you do not line up the decimal points?** Possible answer: I may not compare the digits in the same place-value position correctly.

- **Why do you compare the digits from left to right?** Possible answer: I need to start with the greatest place-value position; the number with the greater digit in the greatest place-value position is greater.

- **What do you do if the digits in the greatest place-value position are the same?** Possible answer: I move to the next lesser place-value position and compare the digits.

▶ Another Way

Discuss how to compare two numbers using a place-value chart.

- **How can you use a place-value chart to compare decimals?** Possible answer: Write the digits in the correct place-value positions, and then compare the digits in each place-value position, starting from the greatest place value.

- **What is another way to state the answer?** Possible answer: The height of Wheeler Mountain is less than the height of Cloud Mountain.

Use Math Talk to focus on students' understanding of the importance of lining up decimal points when comparing decimals.

COMMON CORE

CC.5.NBT.3b Read, write, and compare decimals to thousandths. Compare two decimals to thousandths based on meanings of the digits in each place, using >, =, and < symbols to record the results of comparisons.

Name _____

Lesson **3.3**

Compare and Order Decimals

Essential Question How can you use place value to compare and order decimals?

COMMON CORE STANDARD CC.5.NBT.3b
Understand the place value system.

🔑 UNLOCK the Problem REAL WORLD

▲ The Tetons are located in Grand Teton National Park.

The table lists some of the mountains in the United States that are over two miles high. How does the height of Cloud Mountain in New York compare to the height of Boundary Mountain in Nevada?

Mountain Heights	
Mountain and State	**Height (in miles)**
Boundary, Nevada	2.488
Cloud, New York	2.495
Grand Teton, Wyoming	2.607
Wheeler, New Mexico	2.493

🔑 One Way Use place value.

Line up the decimal points. Start at the left. Compare the digits in each place-value position until the digits are different.

STEP 1 Compare the ones.

2.495
↓
2.488   2 = 2

STEP 2 Compare the tenths.

2.495
↓
2.488   4 ⊜ 4

STEP 3 Compare the hundredths.

2.495
↓
2.488   9 ⊜ 8

Since 9 ⊜ 8, then 2.495 ⊜ 2.488, and 2.488 ⊜ 2.495.

So, the height of Cloud Mountain is __greater than__ the height of Boundary Mountain.

🔑 Another Way Use a place-value chart to compare.

Compare the height of Cloud Mountain to Wheeler Mountain.

Ones	Tenths	Hundredths	Thousandths
2	4	9	5
2	4	9	3

2 = 2   4 = __4__   9 = __9__   5 > __3__

Since 5 ⊜ 3, then 2.495 ⊜ 2.493, and 2.493 ⊜ 2.495.

So, the height of Cloud Mountain is __greater than__ the height of Wheeler Mountain.

Math Talk MATHEMATICAL PRACTICES
Explain why it is important to line up the decimal points when comparing decimals.

Possible explanation: You need to line up the decimal points to make sure that you are comparing digits in the same place-value position.

Chapter 3   113

© Houghton Mifflin Harcourt Publishing Company

Standards Practice 3.3
Common Core   SPIRAL REVIEW

Name _____

Compare and Order Decimals

Lesson **3.3**

COMMON CORE STANDARD CC.5.NBT.3b
Understand the place value system.

Compare. Write <, >, or =.

1. 4.735 ⬖ 4.74
2. 2.549 ⬖ 2.549
3. 3.207 ⬖ 3.027
4. 8.25 ⬖ 8.250
5. 5.871 ⬖ 5.781
6. 9.36 ⬖ 9.359
7. 1.538 ⬖ 1.54
8. 7.036 ⬖ 7.035
9. 6.700 ⬖ 6.7

Order from greatest to least.

10. 3.008; 3.825; 3.09; 3.18

__3.825; 3.18; 3.09; 3.008__

11. 0.275; 0.2; 0.572; 0.725

__0.725; 0.572; 0.275; 0.2__

12. 6.318; 6.32; 6.230; 6.108

__6.32; 6.318; 6.230; 6.108__

13. 0.456; 1.345; 0.645; 0.654

__1.345; 0.654; 0.645; 0.456__

Algebra Find the unknown digit to make each statement true.

14. 2.48 > 2.4 ⬜ 1 > 2.463

__7__

15. 5.723 < 5.72 ⬜ < 5.725

__4__

16. 7.64 < 7. ⬜ 5 < 7.68

__6__

Problem Solving REAL WORLD

17. The completion times for three runners in a 100-yard dash are 9.75 seconds, 9.7 seconds, and 9.675 seconds. Which is the winning time?

__9.675 seconds__

18. In a discus competition, an athlete threw the discus 63.37 meters, 62.95 meters, and 63.7 meters. Order the distances from least to greatest.

__62.95 meters, 63.37 meters, 63.7 meters__

Chapter 3   PS7

Lesson Check (CC.5.NBT.3b)

Jay, Alana, Evan, and Stacey work together to complete a science experiment. The table at the right shows the amount of liquid left in each of their beakers at the end of the experiment.

Student	Amount of liquid (liters)
Jay	0.8
Alana	1.05
Evan	1.2
Stacey	0.75

1. Whose beaker has the greatest amount of liquid left in it?
 (A) Jay   (C) Evan
 (B) Alana   (D) Stacey

2. Whose beaker has the least amount of liquid left in it?
 (A) Jay   (C) Evan
 (B) Alana   (D) Stacey

Spiral Review (CC.5.OA.1, CC.5.OA.2, CC.5.NBT.3a, CC.5.NF.3)

3. Janet walked 3.75 miles yesterday. Which is the word form of 3.75? (Lesson 3.2)
 (A) three and seventy-five tenths
 (B) three hundred seventy-five hundredths
 (C) three hundred seventy-five thousandths
 ● three and seventy-five hundredths

4. A dance school allows a maximum of 15 students per class. If 112 students sign up for dance class, how many classes does the school need to offer to accommodate all the students? (Lesson 2.7)
 (A) 7   (C) 9
 ● 8   (D) 10

5. Which expression has a value of 7? (Lesson 1.12)
 (A) [(29 − 18) + (17 + 8)] ÷ 5
 (B) [(29 − 18) + (17 + 8)] ÷ 4
 (C) [(29 + 18) − (17 + 8)] ÷ 2
 ● [(29 − 18) + (17 − 8)] ÷ 8

6. Cathy cut 2 apples into 6 slices each. She ate 9 slices. Which expression matches the words? (Lesson 1.10)
 ● (2 × 6) − 9
 (B) (6 × 9) − 2
 (C) (9 × 2) − 6
 (D) (9 − 6) × 2

★TEST PREP

PS8

© Houghton Mifflin Harcourt Publishing Company

Order Decimals You can use place value to order decimal numbers.

 Example

Mount Whitney in California is 2.745 miles high, Mount Rainier in Washington is 2.729 miles high, and Mount Harvard in Colorado is 2.731 miles high. Order the heights of these mountains from least to greatest. Which mountain has the least height? Which mountain has the greatest height?

STEP 1

Line up the decimal points. There are the same number of ones. Circle the tenths and compare.

2.⑦45   **Whitney**

2.⑦29   **Rainier**

2.⑦31   **Harvard**

There are the same number of tenths.

STEP 2

Underline the hundredths and compare. Order from least to greatest.

2.7_4_5   **Whitney**

2.7_2_9   **Rainier**

2.7_3_1   **Harvard**

Since ② < ③ < ④ , the heights in order from least to greatest are ___**2.729**___ , ___**2.731**___ , ___**2.745**___ .

So, ___**Mount Rainier**___ has the least height and

___**Mount Whitney**___ has the greatest height.

Math Talk MATHEMATICAL PRACTICES
Explain why you do not have to compare the digits in the thousandths place to order the heights of the 3 mountains.

Possible explanation: Since the digits are all different in the hundredths place, you can order the decimals without comparing the digits in the thousandths place.

Try This! Use a place-value chart.

What is the order of 1.383, 1.321, 1.456, and 1.32 from greatest to least?

- Write each number in the place-value chart. Compare the digits, beginning with the greatest place value.

- Compare the ones. The ones are the same.

- Compare the tenths. 4 > 3.

The greatest number is ___**1.456**___ .
Circle the greatest number in the place-value chart.

- Compare the remaining hundredths. 8 > 2.

The next greatest number is ___**1.383**___ .
Draw a rectangle around the number.

- Compare the remaining thousandths. 1 > 0.

So, the order of the numbers from greatest to least is: ___**1.456; 1.383; 1.321; 1.32**___ .

Ones	•	Tenths	Hundredths	Thousandths
1	•	3	8	3
1	•	3	2	1
1	•	4	5	6
1	•	3	2	0

© Houghton Mifflin Harcourt Publishing Company

114

▶ **Example**

Read and discuss how to order the heights from least to greatest.

- **In Step 1, why do you move to the tenths and compare the digits?** The digits in the ones place are all the same.

- **In Step 2, why are you comparing the digits in the hundredths place?** The digits in the tenths place are all the same.

- **How do you know that 2.729 is the least?** Possible answer: When I compare the digits in the hundredths place, the 2 is the least digit. 2 hundredths is less than 3 hundredths and 4 hundredths.

- **How do you know which decimal is the greatest?** Possible answer: When comparing the hundredths, the digit with the greatest value is the greatest number. 4 is the greatest digit in the hundredths place, so 2.745 is the greatest number.

Use **Math Talk** to focus on students' understanding of ordering decimals.

Try This!

Discuss how to use a place-value chart to order numbers.

- **How can you record 1.32 in the place-value chart to compare digits in the thousandths place? Explain.** I can write a zero in the thousandths place of 1.32, making it 1.320, because it does not change its value.

- **Is it necessary to compare the thousandths? Explain.** Yes; Possible explanation: The numbers 1.321 and 1.320 have the same digits in the ones, tenths, and hundredths place. I need to compare the digits in the thousandths place.

- **How is using place value similar to using a place-value chart?** Possible answer: I compare digits in the same place-value position, moving left to right and starting from the greatest place value.

 COMMON ERRORS

Error Students may use digits that do not have the same place value to compare and order decimals.

Example 6.76 < 6.7_5_9 because 6 < 7

Springboard to Learning Have students write the numbers in a place-value chart to help them compare the digits in the correct place-value positions.

▲ **RtI**

Reteach 3.3

Name _____   Lesson 3.3
Reteach

Compare and Order Decimals

You can use a place-value chart to compare decimals.

Compare. Write <, >, or =.

4.375 ◯ 4.382

Write both numbers in a place-value chart. Then compare the digits, starting with the highest place value. Stop when the digits are different and compare.

Ones	Tenths	Hundredths	Thousandths
4	3	7	5
4	3	8	2

The ones digits The tenths digits The hundredths are the same.   are the same.   digits are different.

The digits are different in the hundredths place.

Since 7 hundredths < 8 hundredths, 4.375 ◯< 4.382.

1. Use the place-value chart to compare the two numbers. What is the greatest place-value position where the digits differ?

Ones	Tenths	Hundredths	Thousandths
2	8	6	5
2	8	6	1

thousandths; 2.865 > 2.861

Compare. Write <, >, or =.

2. 5.37 ◯= 5.370   3. 9.425 ◯> 9.417   4. 7.684 ◯< 7.689

Name the greatest place-value position where the digits differ.
Name the greater number.

5. 8.675; 8.654
hundredths
8.675

6. 3.086; 3.194
tenths
3.194

7. 6.243; 6.247
thousandths
6.247

Order from least to greatest.

8. 5.04; 5.4; 5.406; 5.064
5.04; 5.064; 5.4; 5.406

9. 2.614; 2.146; 2.46; 2.164
2.146; 2.164; 2.46; 2.614

Reteach   R24   Grade 5
© Houghton Mifflin Harcourt Publishing Company

Enrich 3.3

Name _____   Lesson 3.3
Enrich

Order Your Own Decimals

Solve each problem. In each row, use each digit exactly once.
Possible answers are given.

1. Place the digits 0, 2, 5, 8 in each row of the table to create four decimals that are in order from least to greatest.

Ones	Tenths	Hundredths	Thousandths
2	8	5	0
5	8	0	2
8	2	0	5
8	5	2	0

2. Place the digits 1, 3, 6, 9 in each row of the table to create four decimals that are in order from greatest to least.

Ones	Tenths	Hundredths	Thousandths
9	6	3	1
6	9	1	3
3	9	6	1
1	9	6	3

3. Place the digits 0, 1, 4, 7, 8 in each row of the table to create four decimals that are in order from least to greatest.

Tens	Ones	Tenths	Hundredths	Thousandths
1	0	4	7	8
4	1	8	0	7
7	1	8	0	4
8	7	4	1	0

4. Place the digits 2, 3, 6, 8, 9 in each row of the table to create four decimals that are in order from greatest to least.

Tens	Ones	Tenths	Hundredths	Thousandths
9	8	6	3	2
8	9	3	2	6
3	6	2	8	9
2	3	9	6	8

Enrich   E24   Grade 5
© Houghton Mifflin Harcourt Publishing Company

3 PRACTICE

▶ Share and Show • Guided Practice

The first problem connects to the learning model. Have students use the MathBoard to explain their thinking.

Use Exercises 4 and 7 for Quick Check. Students should show their answers for the Quick Check on the MathBoard.

 Quick Check **RtI**

If	a student misses Exercises 4 and 7
Then	**Differentiate Instruction with** • RtI Tier 1 Activity, p. 113B • Reteach 3.3 ☆ Soar to Success Math 8.44

▶ On Your Own • Independent Practice

If students complete Exercises 4 and 7 correctly, they may continue with Independent Practice.

H.O.T. Problems In Exercises 20–22, students must find an unknown digit that makes a true statement with two comparisons.

• **What strategy can you use to find the unknown digit?** Possible answer: I can guess a digit and then check to see if each comparison is true. If it isn't, then I can revise my guess and check again.

Name _____

Share and Show ....

1. Use the place-value chart to compare the two numbers. What is the greatest place-value position where the digits differ?

Ones	•	Tenths	Hundredths	Thousandths
3	•	4	7	2
3	•	4	4	5

   hundredths; 3.472 > 3.445 or 3.445 < 3.472

Compare. Write <, >, or =.

2. 4.563 $>$ 4.536 | 3. 5.640 $=$ 5.64 | ✓ 4. 8.673 $>$ 8.637

Name the greatest place-value position where the digits differ. Name the greater number.

5. 3.579; 3.564 | 6. 9.572; 9.637 | ✓ 7. 4.159; 4.152

   hundredths | tenths | thousandths

   3.579 | 9.637 | 4.159

Order from least to greatest.

8. 4.08; 4.3; 4.803; 4.038 | 9. 1.703; 1.037; 1.37; 1.073

   4.038; 4.08; 4.3; 4.803 | 1.037; 1.073; 1.37; 1.703

On Your Own ....

Compare. Write <, >, or =.

10. 8.72 $=$ 8.720 | 11. 5.4 $>$ 5.243 | 12. 1.036 $<$ 1.306

13. 2.573 $<$ 2.753 | 14. 9.300 $=$ 9.3 | 15. 6.76 $>$ 6.759

Order from greatest to least.

16. 2.007; 2.714; 2.09; 2.97 | 17. 0.386; 0.3; 0.683; 0.836

   2.97; 2.714; 2.09; 2.007 | 0.836; 0.683; 0.386; 0.3

18. 5.249; 5.43; 5.340; 5.209 | 19. 0.678; 1.678; 0.587; 0.687

   5.43; 5.340; 5.249; 5.209 | 1.678; 0.687; 0.678; 0.587

 Algebra Find the unknown digit to make each statement true.

20. 3.59 > 3.5 **8** 1 > 3.572 | 21. 6.837 > 6.83 **6** > 6.835 | 22. 2.45 < 2. **4** 6 < 2.461

© Houghton Mifflin Harcourt Publishing Company

Chapter 3 • Lesson 3 **115**

COMMON CORE PROFESSIONAL DEVELOPMENT

Math Talk in Action

This Math Talk in Action is an example of dialogue for Exercise 17.

Teacher: Explain how you ordered the numbers.

Naomi: I wrote each number in a place-value chart, writing each digit in the correct place-value position. Then I compared the digits from left to right.

Teacher: What happened when you compared the tenths?

Naomi: 8 was the greatest digit, so I knew 0.836 was the greatest number. 6 was the next greatest digit, so I knew 0.683 came second. There were two numbers with 3s in the tenths place, though.

Teacher: How did you compare the numbers that both had 3s in the tenths place?

Naomi: Since the tenths digits were the same, I compared the digits in the hundredths place.

Teacher: For 0.3, what digit did you use to compare the hundredths?

Naomi: I used 0 since writing a zero to the right of a decimal doesn't change its value. So, 0.386 was greater than 0.30 because 8 > 0. The numbers in order from greatest to least are 0.836, 0.683, 0.386, and 0.3.

Teacher: Did anyone use a different method?

Pedro: I got the same answer by aligning the decimal points and comparing the digits in the same place-value positions from left to right.

Teacher: Very good!

115 Chapter 3

Problem Solving

Use the Table for 23–26.

23. In comparing the height of the mountains, which is the greatest place value where the digits differ?

    _____hundredths place_____

24. How does the height of Steele Mountain compare to the height of Blackburn Mountain? Compare the heights using words. **Possible answer:**

    Steele Mountain has a height that is greater

    than the height of Blackburn Mountain.

25. [Write Math] ▶ Explain how to order the height of the mountains from greatest to least. **Possible explanation:**

    Compare the place values from left to right.

    The ones and tenths are the same. Comparing

    the hundredths, 5 > 3 > 0. From greatest to

    least height: Steele, Bona, and Blackburn

26. [H.O.T.] What if the height of Blackburn Mountain were 0.05 mile greater. Would it then be the mountain with the greatest height? Explain.

    Yes; Possible explanation: It would have the

    same digits as Steele in the ones, tenths, and

    hundredths places, but a greater digit in the thousandths place.

27. ⭐ **Test Prep** Mount Logan in the Yukon is 3.702 miles high. Mount McKinley in Alaska is 3.848 miles high and Pico de Orizaba in Mexico is 3.571 miles high. Order these mountains by height from greatest to least.

    (A) Logan, McKinley, Pico de Orizaba

    (B) McKinley, Logan, Pico de Orizaba

    (C) Pico de Orizaba, Logan, McKinley

    (D) Logan, Pico de Orizaba, McKinley

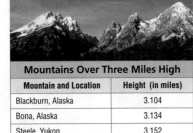

Mountains Over Three Miles High

Mountain and Location	Height (in miles)
Blackburn, Alaska	3.104
Bona, Alaska	3.134
Steele, Yukon	3.152

 SHOW YOUR WORK

© Houghton Mifflin Harcourt Publishing Company

 Model • Reason • Make Sense

▶ **Problem Solving**

In Exercises 23–26, students use information from a table to solve problems involving comparing and ordering decimals.

H.O.T. Problem Exercise 26 requires students to first add 0.05 to the height of Blackburn Mountain and then compare the sum with the other heights in the table.

Test Prep Coach

In Exercise 27, if students selected:

A or D They did not compare place values correctly.
C They ordered from least to greatest instead of from greatest to least.

4 SUMMARIZE

Essential Question

How can you use place value to compare and order decimals? Possible answer: Line up the decimal points of the numbers to be compared or ordered or use a place-value chart. Compare the digits in each place-value position, starting from the greatest place-value position. The digit that is greatest is in the greatest number. If the digits are the same, move to the next lesser place-value position and compare the digits.

Math Journal

Write a word problem that can be solved by ordering three decimals to thousandths. Include a solution.

Lesson 3.3 116

Round Decimals

LESSON AT A GLANCE

Common Core Standard
Understand the place value system.
CC.5.NBT.4 Use place value understanding to round decimals to any place.

Lesson Objective
Round decimals to any place.

Essential Question
How can you use place value to round decimals to a given place?

Materials
MathBoard

Digital Path

MM **HMH Mega Math**

GO MATH! **eStudent Edition**

 **PROFESSIONAL DEVELOPMENT**

About the Math

Teaching for Depth In this lesson, students round decimals to the nearest whole number, tenth, or hundredth using a place-value chart and place value.

Students find that rounding decimals is similar to rounding whole numbers. If the digit to the right of the digit in the rounding place is greater than or equal to 5, then the digit in the rounding place increases by 1 and the digits to its right are dropped. If the digit to the right of the digit in the rounding place is less than 5, then the digit in the rounding place stays the same and the digits to its right are dropped.

Students learn that rounding to the nearest whole number means rounding to the nearest one. The digit in the tenths place determines whether the digit in the rounding place increases by 1 or stays the same.

Learning to round decimals will help students estimate decimal sums and differences later.

 Professional Development Video Podcasts

Daily Routines [Math Board]

Common Core

SPIRAL REVIEW

Problem of the Day

 eTransparency 3.4

Test Prep Jolene, Helen, and Marta need to order hats for the school play. The table shows the measurement around their heads. Which lists the order of the students from smallest to largest head size?

Student	Measurement (inches)
Jolene	21.625
Helen	20.875
Marta	21.25

  Ⓐ Jolene, Helen, Marta

  ● Helen, Marta, Jolene

  © Marta, Helen, Jolene

  Ⓓ Helen, Jolene, Marta

Vocabulary Builder

Materials index cards

Review Definitions Have students review what it means to *round* a number. Put students in groups, and have each group write a definition and an example on an index card. Collect the cards and then discuss the definitions and examples as a class. What makes a good definition? Which examples are most helpful? Then talk about times when rounding is useful.

Differentiated Instruction Activities

ELL Language Support Verbal / Linguistic Small Group

Strategy: Define

- Students can define words by using them in context with their definitions. The word *round* has different meanings. In math, it means to replace a number with one that is simpler and is approximately the same size as the original number.

- Remind students that when they round, they are finding a close approximation.

- Model the sentences, "1.25 rounded to the nearest tenth is 1.3. 1.25 is about 1.3. 1.25 is close to 1.3." Have students repeat the sentences.

- Then have students round several decimals to the nearest tenth, repeating the same sentence pattern each time.

See **ELL** Activity Guide for leveled activities.

Enrich Logical / Mathematical Individual / Partners

- Write the following problem on the board:

_____ rounded to the nearest tenth is 6.5.
Ⓐ 6.43   Ⓒ 6.53
Ⓑ 6.44   Ⓓ 6.59

- Have students find the answer, checking it with a partner. C

- Then have students write similar problems for their partners to solve. Encourage students to write problems involving decimals that round to ones, tenths, and hundredths.

RtI Response to Intervention

Reteach Tier 1 Visual Whole Class / Small Group

Materials Place-Value Charts (see *eTeacher Resources*)

- Write the number 1.574 on the board. Have students write the number in their place-value chart.

- **Let's round 1.574 to the nearest tenth. Which digit is in the tenths place?** 5 Have students circle the 5.

- **Which digit will you look at to determine whether the digit you circled will increase by one or stay the same?** the digit to the right, 7 Have students underline the 7.

- **"Five or more add one more." Do you add one more?** Yes; 7 is greater than 5.

- Repeat with other decimals, rounding to different place values.

Tier 2 Visual / Kinesthetic Small Group

Materials index cards

- Write decimals to thousandths on index cards. Make a stack of 10 cards for the group.

- **Suppose you rounded each decimal to the nearest tenth.**

- **How do you know in which decimals the digit in the tenths place will increase by 1?** The digit in the hundredths place is 5 or greater.

- **How do you know in which decimals the digit in the tenths place will stay the same?** The digit in the hundredths place is less than 5.

- Have students work as a group to sort the cards into two piles. After checking students' work, have them repeat the process by rounding to a different place value.

COMMON CORE

CC.5.NBT.4 Use place value understanding to round decimals to any place.

1 ENGAGE  Math Board

Access Prior Knowledge Write the following number on the board: 45,926.

- **Explain how you can round this number to the nearest thousand.** Possible explanation: I look at the digit to the right of the place I am rounding, 9. Since 9 is greater than 5, I add 1 to the 5 in the thousands place and change the digits in the place values to its right to 0. So, 45,926 rounded to the nearest thousand is 46,000.

2 TEACH and TALK GO Online HMH Mega Math

▶ Unlock the Problem MATHEMATICAL PRACTICES

Read and discuss the problem about the length of the smallest frog in the world.

- **What number are you rounding?** 0.386
- **To what place are you rounding?** hundredth

▶ One Way

Discuss how to use a place-value chart to round decimals.

- **Why do you circle the 8?** Possible answer: This is the digit in the place to which I want to round.

- **Why do you underline the 6?** Possible answer: This digit will tell me whether to increase the circled digit by 1 or keep it the same. If it is greater than or equal to 5, then I increase the digit in the rounding place by 1. If it less than 5, then I keep the digit in the rounding place the same.

- **How does a place-value chart help you round?** Possible answer: I can easily find the digit in the rounding place and the digit to its right that tells me whether to increase the digit in the rounding place or keep it the same.

▶ Another Way

Discuss how to round using place value.

- **In Part A, which digit is in the place to which you are rounding?** 3

- **How will you decide whether to increase the digit in the rounding place or keep it the same?** Possible answer: I will look at the digit to the right of the 3. It's a 7, which is greater than 5. So, I will increase 3 by 1 and drop the digits to its right.

- **In Part B, which digit is in the place to which you are rounding?** 4

- **How will you decide whether to increase the digit in the rounding place or keep it the same?** Possible answer: I will look at the digit to the right of the 4. It's a 3, which is less than 5. So, I will keep the 4 the same and drop the digits to its right.

Name _____

Lesson **3.4**

Round Decimals

COMMON CORE STANDARD CC.5.NBT.4
Understand the place value system.

Essential Question How can you use place value to round decimals to a given place?

🔓 UNLOCK the Problem REAL WORLD

The Gold Frog of South America is one of the smallest frogs in the world. It is 0.386 of an inch long. What is this length rounded to the nearest hundredth of an inch?

- Underline the length of the Gold Frog.
- Is the frog's length about the same as the length or the width of a large paper clip?

the width of a large paper clip

🔑 One Way Use a place-value chart.

- Write the number in a place-value chart and circle the digit in the place value to which you want to round.

- In the place-value chart, underline the digit to the right of the place to which you are rounding.

- If the digit to the right is less than 5, the digit in the place value to which you are rounding stays the same. If the digit to the right is 5 or greater, the digit in the rounding place increases by 1.

- Drop the digits after the place to which you are rounding.

So, to the nearest hundredth of an inch, a Gold Frog is

about ___0.39___ of an inch long.

Ones	Tenths	Hundredths	Thousandths
0	3	⑧	6

Think: Does the digit in the rounding place stay the same or increase by 1?

🔑 Another Way Use place value.

The Little Grass Frog is the smallest frog in North America. It is 0.437 of an inch long.

A What is the length of the frog to the nearest hundredth of an inch?

0.437   7 > 5
↓
0.44

So, to the nearest hundredth of an inch, the frog

is about ___0.44___ of an inch long.

B What is the length of the frog to the nearest tenth of an inch?

0.437   3 < 5
↓
0.4

So, to the nearest tenth of an inch, the frog is

about ___0.4___ of an inch long.

© Houghton Mifflin Harcourt Publishing Company

Name _____

Standards Practice 3.4

Round Decimals

COMMON CORE STANDARD CC.5.NBT.4
Understand the place value system.

Lesson **3.4**

Write the place value of the underlined digit. Round each number to the place of the underlined digit.

1. 0.7̲82
   tenths
   0.8

2. 4̲.735
   ones
   5

3. 2.3̲48
   tenths
   2.3

4. 0.5̲06
   hundredths
   0.51

5. 15.1̲86
   tenths
   15.2

6. 8.46̲5
   hundredths
   8.47

Name the place value to which each number was rounded.

7. 0.546 to 0.55
   hundredths

8. 4.805 to 4.8
   tenths

9. 6.493 to 6
   ones

10. 1.974 to 2.0
    tenths

11. 7.709 to 8
    ones

12. 14.637 to 15
    ones

Round 7.954 to the place named.

13. tenths
    8.0

14. hundredths
    7.95

15. ones
    8

Round 18.194 to the place named.

16. tenths
    18.2

17. hundredths
    18.19

18. ones
    18

Problem Solving REAL WORLD

19. The population density of Montana is 6.699 people per square mile. What is the population density per square mile of Montana rounded to the nearest whole number?

    7 people per square mile

20. Alex's batting average is 0.346. What is his batting average rounded to the nearest hundredth?

    0.35

Common Core SPIRAL REVIEW

Lesson Check (CC.5.NBT.4)

1. Ms. Ari buys and sells diamonds. She has a diamond that weighs 1.825 carats. What is the weight of Ms. Ari's diamond rounded to the nearest hundredth?
   - (A) 1.8 carats
   - (B) 1.82 carats
   - ● 1.83 carats
   - (D) 1.9 carats

2. A machinist uses a special tool to measure the diameter of a small pipe. The measurement tool reads 0.276 inch. What is this measure rounded to the nearest tenth?
   - (A) 0.2 inch
   - (B) 0.27 inch
   - (C) 0.28 inch
   - ● 0.3 inch

Spiral Review (CC.5.NBT.1, CC.5.NBT.2, CC.5.NBT.3b, CC.5.NBT.6)

3. Four ice skaters participate in an ice skating competition. The table shows their scores. Who has the highest score? (Lesson 3.3)

Name	Points
Natasha	75.03
Taylor	75.39
Rowena	74.98
Suki	75.3

   - (A) Natasha
   - ● Taylor
   - (C) Rowena
   - (D) Suki

4. Which of the following statements is true about the relationship between the decimals 0.09 and 0.9? (Lesson 3.1)
   - (A) 0.09 is equal to 0.9
   - (B) 0.09 is 10 times as much as 0.9.
   - ● 0.9 is $\frac{1}{10}$ of 0.09.
   - (D) 0.09 is $\frac{1}{10}$ of 0.9

5. The population of Foxville is about 12×10^3 people. Which is another way to write this number? (Lesson 1.5)
   - (A) 120
   - (B) 1,200
   - ● 12,000
   - (D) 120,000

6. Joseph needs to find the quotient of 3,216 ÷ 8. In which place is the first digit in the quotient? (Lesson 2.1)
   - (A) ones
   - (B) tens
   - ● hundreds
   - (D) thousands

Example

The Goliath Frog is the largest frog in the world. It is found in the country of Cameroon in West Africa. The Goliath Frog can grow to be 11.815 inches long. How long is the Goliath Frog to the nearest inch?

STEP 1 Write 11.815 in the place-value chart.

Tens	Ones	Tenths	Hundredths	Thousandths
1	①	8	1	5

STEP 2 Find the place to which you want to round. Circle the digit.

STEP 3 Underline the digit to the right of the place value to which you are rounding. Then round.

> Think: Does the digit in the rounding place stay the same or increase by 1?

So, to the nearest inch, the Goliath Frog is about ___12___ inches long.

- Explain why any number less than 12.5 and greater than or equal to 11.5 would round to 12 when rounded to the nearest whole number.

  Possible explanation: With any digit less than 5 in the tenths place, the digit in the ones

  place remains unchanged. With any digit greater than or equal to 5 in the tenths place, the

  digit in the ones place increases by 1.

Try This! Round. 14.603

Ⓐ To the nearest hundredth:

Tens	Ones	Tenths	Hundredths	Thousandths
1	4	6	⓪	3

Circle and underline the digits as you did above to help you round to the nearest hundredth.

So, 14.603 rounded to the nearest hundredth is ___14.60___.

Ⓑ To the nearest whole number:

Tens	Ones	Tenths	Hundredths	Thousandths
1	④	6	0	3

Circle and underline the digits as you did above to help you round to the nearest whole number.

So, 14.603 rounded to the nearest whole number is ___15___.

118

© Houghton Mifflin Harcourt Publishing Company

▶ **Example**

- **In Step 2, why do you circle the 1?** Possible answer: I am rounding to the nearest inch, so I circle the digit in the ones place.

- **How is rounding decimals similar to rounding whole numbers?** Possible answer: In both cases, you look at the digit in the rounding place and at the digit to its right to determine whether the digit in the rounding place increases by 1 or stays the same.

Try This!

Discuss what happens when there is a zero in the place to which you are rounding.

- **What is the digit in the hundredths place?** zero

- **Will the digit in the rounding place increase by 1 or stay the same when rounding to the nearest hundredth? Explain.** Possible answer: The digit to the right is 3. 3 is less than 5, so you keep the zero in the hundredths place the same.

- **Do you need to write the zero in the hundredths place in your answer? Explain.** Yes; Possible explanation: I need to round to hundredths, so I need to show a digit in that place value in my answer.

Discuss what it means to round to the nearest whole number.

- **How do you know what place to round to when rounding to the nearest whole number?** Possible answer: The nearest whole number would mean rounding to the ones place; there wouldn't be any decimal places in the rounded number.

Reteach 3.4

Enrich 3.4

 COMMON ERRORS

Error Students may round to the wrong place value.

Example 5.683 rounded to the nearest hundredth is 5.7.

Springboard to Learning Encourage students to circle the digit in the place they are rounding to and then look at the digit to its right.

3 PRACTICE

▶ Share and Show • Guided Practice

The first problems connect to the learning model.

Use Exercises 2 and 6 for Quick Check.

 Quick Check

If → a student misses Exercises 2 and 6

 Then → **Differentiate Instruction with**
- RtI Tier 1 Activity, p. 117B
- Reteach 3.4
- ✸ Soar to Success Math 25.23

▶ On Your Own • Independent Practice

If students complete Exercises 2 and 6 correctly, they may continue with Independent Practice.

In Exercise 19, students must explain what happens when rounding when there is a 9 in the place to which they are rounding.

- **How would you round to the nearest hundredth?** Possible answer: I would look at the digit in the thousandths place, 9. Since 9 is greater than 5, I would increase the digit in the hundredths place by 1. 9 + 1 = 10. That would add a 1 to the tenths place. 9 + 1 = 10. This adds a 1 to the ones place. 4 + 1 = 5. So, I get 5.00.

Name _____

Share and Show MATH BOARD ·······················

Write the place value of the underlined digit. Round each number to the place of the underlined digit.

1. 0.6<u>7</u>3

hundredths
_____
0.67

☑ **2.** 4.<u>2</u>82

tenths
_____
4.3

3. 1<u>2</u>.917

ones
_____
13

Name the place value to which each number was rounded.

4. 0.982 to 0.98

hundredths

5. 3.695 to 4

ones

☑ **6.** 7.486 to 7.5

tenths

On Your Own ·································

Write the place value of the underlined digit. Round each number to the place of the underlined digit.

7. 0.<u>5</u>92

tenths
_____
0.6

8. <u>6</u>.518

ones
_____
7

9. 0.8<u>0</u>9

hundredths
_____
0.81

10. 3.<u>3</u>34

tenths
_____
3.3

11. 12.<u>0</u>74

tenths
_____
12.1

12. 4.4<u>9</u>4

hundredths
_____
4.49

Name the place value to which each number was rounded.

13. 0.328 to 0.33

hundredths

14. 2.607 to 2.61

hundredths

15. 12.583 to 13

ones

Round 16.748 to the place named.

16. tenths ___16.7___

17. hundredths ___16.75___

18. ones ___17___

19. [Write Math] ▶ Explain what happens when you round 4.999 to the nearest tenth. Possible explanation: Since there is a 9 in the hundredths place, the number in the tenths place will increase by 1. Since 9 + 1 = 10, a 0 will go in the tenths place and the 1 will be added to the 4 in the ones place making the answer 5.0.

© Houghton Mifflin Harcourt Publishing Company

Chapter 3 • Lesson 4 119

Problem Solving REAL WORLD

Use the table for 20–22.

20. The speeds of two insects when rounded to the nearest whole number are the same. Which two insects are they?

    bumblebee and honeybee

21. What is the speed of the housefly rounded to the nearest hundredth?

    1.97 meters per second

22. ⚡H.O.T. What's the Error? Mark said that the speed of a dragonfly rounded to the nearest tenth was 6.9 meters per second. Is he correct? If not, what is his error?

    Mark is not correct. He should have

    written a 0 in the tenths place and

    rounded the ones to 7.

23. ⚡H.O.T. Write Math ▶ A rounded number for the speed of an insect is 5.67 meters per second. What are the fastest and slowest speeds to the thousandths that could round to 5.67? Explain.

    The fastest speed is 5.674. The slowest

    speed is 5.665. Possible explanation: Any

    number greater than 5.674 would round to

    5.68. Any number less than 5.665 would

    round to 5.66.

24. ⭐ Test Prep To which place value is the number rounded?

    6.706 to 6.71

    Ⓐ ones   ● hundredths

    Ⓑ tenths   Ⓓ thousandths

Insect Speeds (meters per second)	
Insect	**Speed**
Dragonfly	6.974
Horsefly	3.934
Bumblebee	2.861
Honeybee	2.548
Housefly	1.967

SHOW YOUR WORK

© Houghton Mifflin Harcourt Publishing Company

FOR EXTRA PRACTICE:
Standards Practice Book, p. P77

▶ ## Problem Solving (MATHEMATICAL PRACTICES)

In Exercises 20–22, students use information from a table to solve problems involving rounding decimals.

In Exercise 23, students need to find the least and greatest numbers that would round to 5.67.

⭐ Test Prep Coach

Test Prep Coach helps teachers to identify common errors that students can make.

In Exercise 24, if students selected:

A, B, or **D**   They identified the wrong place value.

4 SUMMARIZE (MATHEMATICAL PRACTICES)

Essential Question

How can you use place value to round decimals to a given place? Possible answer: Find the digit in the place to which you are rounding. Then look at the digit to its right. If that digit is greater than or equal to 5, increase the digit in the place to which you are rounding by 1 and drop the digits to its right. If the digit to the right is less than 5, keep the digit in the place value you are rounding to the same and drop the digits to its right.

Math Journal

Describe how to round 3.987 to the nearest tenth.

 Differentiated Instruction INDEPENDENT ACTIVITIES

Grab-and-Go!™

Differentiated Centers Kit

Activities
Do We Decimal?

 Students complete orange Activity Card 4 by drawing models of decimals and representing the models as decimals and as fractions.

Literature
Dewey and His Decimals

Students read about the Dewey Decimal system used to order books in the library.

Games
Decimal Challenge

 Students name a decimal greater than, less than, or equal to the given decimal.

Digital Path

✉ Animated Math Models
iT iTools
〽 HMH Mega Math
⭐ Soar to Success Math
GO eStudent Edition

Lesson 3.4   120

Investigate • Decimal Addition

LESSON AT A GLANCE

Common Core Standard
Perform operations with multi-digit whole numbers and with decimals to hundredths.
CC.5.NBT.7 Add, subtract, multiply, and divide decimals to hundredths, using concrete models or drawings and strategies based on place value, properties of operations, and/or the relationship between addition and subtraction; relate the strategy to a written method and explain the reasoning used.

Lesson Objective
Model decimal addition using base-ten blocks.

Essential Question
How can you use base-ten blocks to model decimal addition?

Materials MathBoard, base-ten blocks

Digital Path

GO eStudent Edition

Daily Routines
Math Board

Common Core
SPIRAL REVIEW

Problem of the Day
eTransparency 3.5

Test Prep Maria made 4 pies for the school carnival. She cut each pie into 8 slices. If she sold 27 slices, how many slices did she have left over?

    Ⓐ   1
    ●   5
    Ⓒ   16
    Ⓓ   32

COMMON CORE
MATHEMATICAL PRACTICES

Using Base-Ten Blocks

- In their previous work with place value and whole numbers, students used base-ten blocks to model whole numbers. Flats modeled hundreds, longs modeled tens, and small cubes modeled ones. For example, the model at the upper right represents 125, a whole number.

- In this lesson, the base-ten blocks will be used to model decimal place values. As shown at the right, we will use flats to model ones, longs to model tenths, and small cubes to model hundredths. For example, the model at the lower right represents 1.25, a decimal number in hundredths.

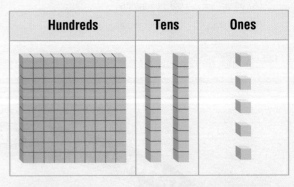

Hundreds	Tens	Ones

Ones	Tenths	Hundredths

Differentiated Instruction Activities

ELL Language Support
Kinesthetic
Small Group

Strategy: Explore Context

Materials base-ten blocks

- In earlier chapters, the flat had a value of 100, the long had a value of 10, and the small cube had a value of 1.

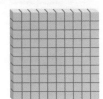 

One   One tenth   One hundredth

- In this lesson, these same blocks have different values. Have students practice using these different values by modeling decimals such as four and three hundredths.

See **ELL** Activity Guide for leveled activities.

Enrich
Visual
Individual

Materials base-ten blocks

- Have students choose three decimal numbers from the lesson.

$0.27 + 2.5 + 0.73 = $

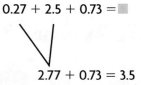

$2.77 + 0.73 = 3.5$

- Students should add the three numbers using base-ten blocks.

- Have students start by adding two of the three numbers that they chose.

- Students should then add that sum to the third number.

RtI Response to Intervention

Reteach Tier 1
Visual
Whole Class / Small Group

Write the expression $0.3 + 0.57$ on the board.

- Discuss with students how to solve the problem.

- Have students discuss how they could use the relationship between decimals and fractions to solve the problem. Students' responses should include an explanation that tenths and hundredths can be represented with fractions and decimals. $0.3 + 0.57$ can be written as $\frac{3}{10} + \frac{57}{100}$.

- **Explain how you can solve the problem using fractions.** Possible answer: I can write the decimals as fractions and add them; $\frac{3}{10} + \frac{57}{100} = \frac{30}{100} + \frac{57}{100} = \frac{87}{100}$. Then I can rewrite the sum as a decimal; $\frac{87}{100} = 0.87$.

- **Have students find $1.25 + 0.4$.** $1\frac{25}{100} + \frac{40}{100} = 1\frac{65}{100}$, or 1.65

Tier 2
Visual / Kinesthetic
Small Group

Materials color pencils, Decimal Models (see *eTeacher Resources*)

- Present this problem: $0.3 + 0.4$. Hold up a tenths decimal model for students. Explain that each column represents 1 tenth. There are 10 tenths, so the entire square represents 1.

- Have students shade 3 tenths of the model. To show addition, use a different color to shade 4 tenths more. **How many tenths are colored altogether?** 7 tenths Have students record the sum $0.3 + 0.4 = 0.7$.

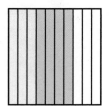

- Have students find $0.5 + 0.2$. When students have mastered adding tenths, repeat the activity with the hundredths decimal model. Have students find $0.21 + 0.15$. 0.36

1 ENGAGE

Materials base-ten blocks

Access Prior Knowledge On the board, write the addition problem shown below.

$$\begin{array}{r} 34 \\ +\ 27 \\ \hline \end{array}$$

Have students explain and demonstrate the regrouping that is needed to complete the addition problem.

2 TEACH and TALK

▶ **Investigate** MATHEMATICAL PRACTICES

Materials base-ten blocks

After students complete the activity, ask them to formulate generalizations that describe when and how to regroup during decimal addition. Possible answers: Regroup when the sum of any place value is 10 or more; regroup 10 hundredths as 1 tenth and 10 tenths as 1 one.

▶ **Draw Conclusions**

H.O.T. Problem For Exercise 2, there are different ways to conclude that the sum of the numbers will be greater than 1; encourage a variety of explanations.

121 Chapter 3

 COMMON CORE CC.5.NBT.7 Add, subtract, multiply, and divide decimals to hundredths, using concrete models or drawings and strategies based on place value, properties of operations, and/or the relationship between addition and subtraction; relate the strategy to a written method and explain the reasoning used.

Name _____

Lesson 3.5

Decimal Addition

COMMON CORE STANDARD CC.5.NBT.7
Perform operations with multi-digit whole numbers and with decimals to hundredths.

Essential Question How can you use base-ten blocks to model decimal addition?

CONNECT You can use base-ten blocks to help you find decimal sums.

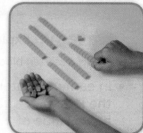

1	0.1	0.01
one	one tenth	one hundredth

Investigate

Materials ■ base-ten blocks

A. Use base-ten blocks to model the sum of 0.34 and 0.27.

B. Add the hundredths first by combining them.
 • Do you need to regroup the hundredths? Explain.

 Yes. Possible explanation: 7 hundredths +

 4 hundredths = 11 hundredths, which is greater

 than 9 hundredths.

C. Add the tenths by combining them.
 • Do you need to regroup the tenths? Explain.

 No. Possible explanation: 3 tenths + 2 tenths +

 1 regrouped tenth = 6 tenths, which is not greater

 than 9 tenths.

D. Record the sum. 0.34 + 0.27 = __0.61__

Draw Conclusions

1. What if you combine the tenths first and then the hundredths? Explain how you would regroup.

 Possible explanation: I would still regroup the hundredths the same way by exchanging

 10 hundredths for 1 tenth and then adding the regrouped tenth to the combined tenths.

2. **H.O.T.** Synthesize If you add two decimals that are each greater than 0.5, will the sum be less than or greater than 1.0? Explain.

 The sum will be greater than 1.0. Possible explanation: Since 0.5 + 0.5 = 1.0, adding

 together two decimals greater than 0.5 will give you a sum greater than 1.0.

© Houghton Mifflin Harcourt Publishing Company

Chapter 3 121

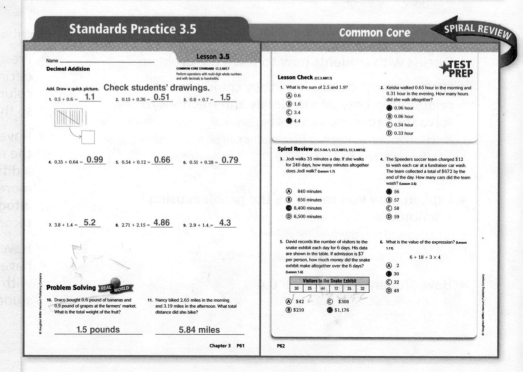

Standards Practice 3.5

Common Core SPIRAL REVIEW

Name _____

Lesson 3.5

Decimal Addition

COMMON CORE STANDARD CC.5.NBT.7
Perform operations with multi-digit whole numbers and with decimals to hundredths.

Add. Draw a quick picture. Check students' drawings.

1. 0.5 + 0.6 = __1.1__   2. 0.15 + 0.36 = __0.51__   3. 0.8 + 0.7 = __1.5__

4. 0.35 + 0.64 = __0.99__   5. 0.54 + 0.12 = __0.66__   6. 0.51 + 0.28 = __0.79__

7. 3.8 + 1.4 = __5.2__   8. 2.71 + 2.15 = __4.86__   9. 2.9 + 1.4 = __4.3__

Problem Solving REAL WORLD

10. Draco bought 0.6 pound of bananas and 0.9 pound of grapes at the farmers' market. What is the total weight of the fruit?

 __1.5 pounds__

11. Nancy biked 2.65 miles in the morning and 3.19 miles in the afternoon. What total distance did she bike?

 __5.84 miles__

Chapter 3 P61

Lesson Check (CC.5.NBT.7)

1. What is the sum of 2.5 and 1.9?
 Ⓐ 0.6
 Ⓑ 1.6
 Ⓒ 3.4
 ● 4.4

2. Keisha walked 0.65 hour in the morning and 0.31 hour in the evening. How many hours did she walk altogether?
 ● 0.96 hour
 Ⓑ 0.86 hour
 Ⓒ 0.34 hour
 Ⓓ 0.33 hour

Spiral Review (CC.5.OA.1, CC.5.NBT.5, CC.5.NBT.6)

3. Jodi walks 35 minutes a day. If she walks for 240 days, how many minutes altogether does Jodi walk? (Lesson 1.7)
 Ⓐ 840 minutes
 Ⓑ 850 minutes
 ● 8,400 minutes
 Ⓓ 8,500 minutes

4. The Speeders soccer team charged $12 to wash each car at a fundraiser car wash. The team collected a total of $672 by the end of the day. How many cars did the team wash? (Lesson 2.6)
 ● 56
 Ⓑ 57
 Ⓒ 58
 Ⓓ 59

5. David records the number of visitors to the snake exhibit each day for 6 days. His data are shown in the table. If admission is $7 per person, how much money did the snake exhibit make altogether over the 6 days? (Lesson 1.6)

Visitors to the Snake Exhibit					
30	25	44	12	25	32

 Ⓐ $42   Ⓒ $308
 Ⓑ $210   ● $1,176

6. What is the value of the expression? (Lesson 1.11)

 $6 + 18 \div 3 \times 4$

 Ⓐ 2
 ● 30
 Ⓒ 32
 Ⓓ 48

P62

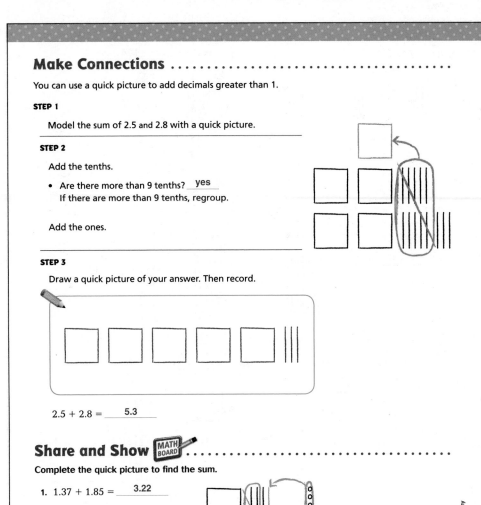

Make Connections
You can use a quick picture to add decimals greater than 1.

STEP 1

Model the sum of 2.5 and 2.8 with a quick picture.

STEP 2

Add the tenths.

• Are there more than 9 tenths? __yes__
  If there are more than 9 tenths, regroup.

Add the ones.

STEP 3

Draw a quick picture of your answer. Then record.

$2.5 + 2.8 =$ __5.3__

Share and Show [MATH BOARD]
Complete the quick picture to find the sum.

1. $1.37 + 1.85 =$ __3.22__

Possible explanation: I know that the decimal point is placed between the ones and tenths places.

[Math Talk] MATHEMATICAL PRACTICES
Explain how you know where to write the decimal point in the sum.

© Houghton Mifflin Harcourt Publishing Company

122

▶ **Make Connections**

Step 1 Focus students' attention on the drawn quick picture. Check to make sure they understand that the squares represent the ones and the sticks represent the tenths.

Step 2 Ask students to describe why you need to regroup when you combine the tenths. There are more than 9 tenths.

Step 3 Ask students to tell what place value each part of their picture represents. The squares represent the ones, and the sticks represent the tenths.

Go Deeper MATHEMATICAL PRACTICES

• Suppose you used base-ten blocks to add three decimal numbers, and there were 20 small cubes in your answer. How would you regroup the 20 small cubes? Possible answer: If 10 small cubes = 1 long, then 20 small cubes = 2 longs; I would replace the 20 small cubes with 2 longs.

3 PRACTICE [Math Board]

▶ **Share and Show • Guided Practice**

The first problem connects to the learning model. Have students use the MathBoard to explain their thinking.

Use Math Talk to focus on students' understanding of writing the decimal point in the sum. Give them an opportunity to discuss, and then state, a general rule.

 COMMON ERRORS

Error Students place the decimal point in a sum incorrectly.

Example After Step 3, students write 0.53 or 53. for the answer.

Springboard to Learning A quick picture for the addition involves drawing squares and sticks. Prompt students to write a decimal point after drawing the squares and before drawing the sticks.

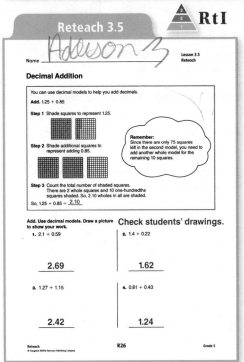

△ RtI

Reteach 3.5

Name __Adelson 3__   Lesson 3.5 Reteach

Decimal Addition

You can use decimal models to help you add decimals.
Add. 1.25 + 0.85

Step 1 Shade squares to represent 1.25.

Step 2 Shade additional squares to represent adding 0.85.

Remember:
Since there are only 75 squares left in the second model, you need to add another whole model for the remaining 10 squares.

Step 3 Count the total number of shaded squares. There are 2 whole squares and 10 one-hundredths squares shaded. So, 2.10 wholes in all are shaded.

So, 1.25 + 0.85 = __2.10__

Add. Use decimal models. Draw a picture to show your work.   Check students' drawings.

1. 2.1 + 0.59   2. 1.4 + 0.22

__2.69__   __1.62__

3. 1.27 + 1.15   4. 0.81 + 0.43

__2.42__   __1.24__

Reteach   R26   Grade 5
© Houghton Mifflin Harcourt Publishing Company

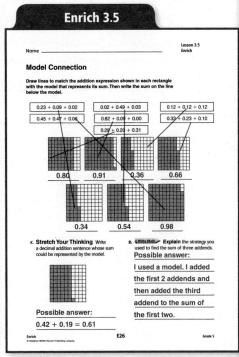

Enrich 3.5

Name ___   Lesson 3.5 Enrich

Model Connection

Draw lines to match the addition expression shown in each rectangle with the model that represents its sum. Then write the sum on the line below the model.

0.23 + 0.09 + 0.02	0.02 + 0.49 + 0.03	0.12 + 0.12 + 0.12
0.45 + 0.47 + 0.06	0.82 + 0.09 + 0.00	0.33 + 0.23 + 0.10
	0.29 + 0.20 + 0.31	

0.80   0.91   0.36   0.66

0.34   0.54   0.98

1. **Stretch Your Thinking** Write a decimal addition sentence whose sum could be represented by the model.

Possible answer:
0.42 + 0.19 = 0.61

2. **Write Math** **Explain** the strategy you used to find the sum of three addends.
Possible answer:
I used a model. I added the first 2 addends and then added the third addend to the sum of the first two.

Enrich   E26   Grade 5
© Houghton Mifflin Harcourt Publishing Company

Lesson 3.5 122

Exercise 2 requires regrouping tenths. Have students use the MathBoard to explain their thinking.

Use Exercises 6 and 7 for **Quick Check**. Students should show their answers for the Quick Check on the MathBoard.

Use **Math Talk** to focus on students' understanding of decimal addition. Make sure the explanations include the idea that regrouping is needed because there are more than 9 tenths.

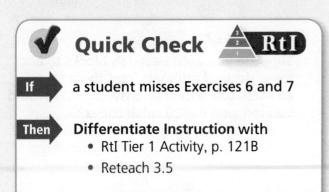

If	a student misses Exercises 6 and 7
Then	**Differentiate Instruction with** • RtI Tier 1 Activity, p. 121B • Reteach 3.5

Go Deeper

MATHEMATICAL PRACTICES

• **If you used only small cubes, how many small cubes would you need to model the sum in Exercise 7? Explain.** 323 small cubes; Each small cube represents one hundredth.
$100 + 100 + 100 + 10 + 10 + 3 = 323$

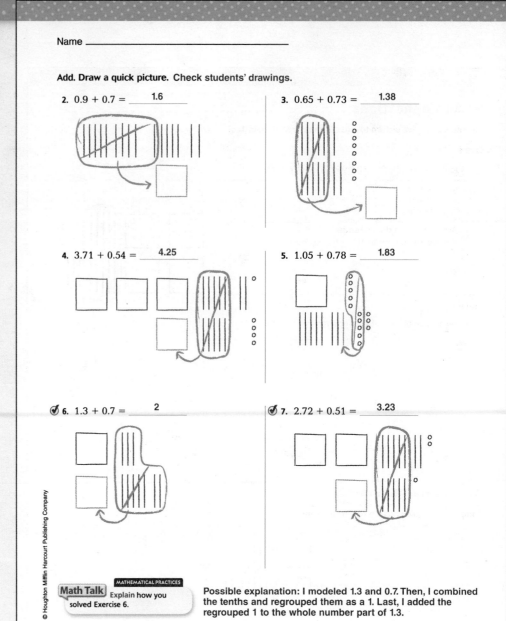

Name _____

Add. Draw a quick picture. Check students' drawings.

2. $0.9 + 0.7 =$ ___1.6___

3. $0.65 + 0.73 =$ ___1.38___

4. $3.71 + 0.54 =$ ___4.25___

5. $1.05 + 0.78 =$ ___1.83___

6. $1.3 + 0.7 =$ ___2___

7. $2.72 + 0.51 =$ ___3.23___

© Houghton Mifflin Harcourt Publishing Company

Math Talk MATHEMATICAL PRACTICES
Explain how you solved Exercise 6.

Possible explanation: I modeled 1.3 and 0.7. Then, I combined the tenths and regrouped them as a 1. Last, I added the regrouped 1 to the whole number part of 1.3.

COMMON CORE
PROFESSIONAL DEVELOPMENT

Mathematical Practices in Your Classroom

CC.K–12.MP.3 Construct viable arguments and critique the reasoning of others.

Evaluating two possible responses to one problem, as in Exercise 8, helps students identify errors in reasoning and clarify their own reasoning for the solution. Have students explain their responses to both Robyn's work and Jim's work to a partner. Remind them to look for all the steps that should be present in the work when determining correctness.

Provide the following sentence starters to help students form their arguments and critique the reasoning in Exercise 8:

• I can see that ___ made a mistake in reasoning because he/she did not ___.

• ___'s reasoning is correct because the ___ were regrouped and added to the ___.

Guide students to use the statements to help them evaluate the problems. Suggest students use similar statements to critique their own work.

Problem Solving

H.O.T. Sense or Nonsense?

8. Robyn and Jim used quick pictures to model 1.85 + 2.73.

Robyn's Work	Jim's Work
	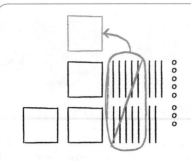

Robyn's Work

1.85 + 2.73 = 3.158

Does Robyn's work make sense?
Explain your reasoning.

No. Robyn's work does not make sense.

Possible explanation: She didn't regroup

10 tenths as 1 one, so she wrote 158

thousandths rather than adding the

regrouped 1 to the other whole numbers.

Jim's Work

1.85 + 2.73 = 4.58

Does Jim's work make sense?
Explain your reasoning.

Yes. Jim's work makes sense. Possible

explanation: He regrouped 10 tenths as

1 one and then added it to the other

whole numbers.

- **Explain** how you would help Robyn understand that regrouping is important when adding decimals.

  Possible explanation: I would explain that regrouping is important because place value

  is based on groups of 10. So, when you have 10 or more of a place value, you regroup.

124 FOR MORE PRACTICE:
Standards Practice Book, pp. P61–P62

▶ **Problem Solving**

H.O.T. Problem In Exercise 8, before students classify each solution, have them contrast the two ways the quick pictures were used.

- **How is the way that Robyn used quick pictures to find the answer different from the way Jim used quick pictures?** Possible answer: Robyn drew each addend without regrouping. Jim used quick pictures to show the sum of the place values after regrouping.

4 SUMMARIZE

Essential Question

How can you use base-ten blocks to model decimal addition? Possible answer: Model each addend using flats, longs, and small cubes. Add the hundredths and, if necessary, regroup every 10 hundredths as 1 tenth. Add the tenths and, if necessary, regroup every 10 tenths as 1 one.

Math Journal

Explain why drawing a quick picture is helpful when adding decimals.

Differentiated Instruction · INDEPENDENT ACTIVITIES

Grab-and-Go!
Differentiated Centers Kit

Activities
Decimal Display

Students complete purple Activity Card 5 by using 10 × 10 grids to model adding decimals.

Activities
Get Around!

Students complete blue Activity Card 5 by adding decimals to find the perimeter of classroom objects.

Literature
A Hundredth of a Second

Students read about Olympic events in which competitors' times are just tenths or hundredths of a second apart.

Digital Path

- Animated Math Models
- iT iTools
- HMH Mega Math
- Soar to Success Math
- eStudent Edition

Investigate • Decimal Subtraction

LESSON AT A GLANCE

Common Core Standard
Perform operations with multi-digit whole numbers and with decimals to hundredths.
CC.5.NBT.7 Add, subtract, multiply, and divide decimals to hundredths, using concrete models or drawings and strategies based on place value, properties of operations, and/or the relationship between addition and subtraction; relate the strategy to a written method and explain the reasoning used.

Lesson Objective
Model decimal subtraction using base-ten blocks.

Essential Question
How can you use base-ten blocks to model decimal subtraction?

Materials
MathBoard, base-ten blocks

Digital Path

 eStudent Edition

 COMMON CORE
PROFESSIONAL DEVELOPMENT

About the Math

Teaching for Depth Frequently throughout this lesson and chapter, remind students that when you subtract decimal numbers, you regroup the same way you regroup whole numbers. For example, if there are not enough tens to subtract, you regroup 1 hundred as 10 tens. In the same way, if there are not enough hundredths to subtract, you regroup 1 tenth as 10 hundredths. In other words, for both decimal and whole numbers, you regroup 1 of the greater unit as 10 of the lesser unit.

Throughout our base-ten number system, 1 of a larger unit is equivalent to 10 of the next smaller unit, and this equivalent relationship forms the foundation of regrouping.

 PODCASTING
Professional Development Video Podcasts

Daily Routines Math Board

Common Core

SPIRAL REVIEW

Problem of the Day
 eTransparency **3.6**

Test Prep Which property is being used in this problem?

$$549 \div 9 = (540 \div 9) + (9 \div 9)$$

(A) Associative Property
(B) Commutative Property
(C) Identity Property
(D) Distributive Property

Fluency Builder

Skills Practice Have students find the following differences.

1. $84 - 56$ 28
2. $282 - 147$ 135
3. $56 - 32$ 24
4. $62 - 18$ 44
5. $11 - 4$ 7
6. $264 - 148$ 116
7. $341 - 174$ 167
8. $84 - 57$ 27
9. $93 - 38$ 55
10. $271 - 134$ 137
11. $405 - 161$ 244
12. $137 - 52$ 85

Differentiated Instruction Activities

ELL Language Support
Kinesthetic
Small Group

Strategy: Describe

Materials base-ten blocks

- Students define the word *regroup* by using it in context and by matching visuals to the definition.

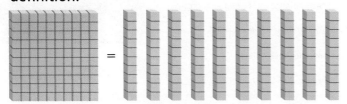

- Have students show how they can regroup by trading in a flat (1) for ten longs (0.1). Explain that *regrouping* means the same as *trading in*.
- Have students model subtraction problems with the base-ten blocks, emphasizing the words *regroup* and *trade in*.

See ELL Activity Guide for leveled activities.

Enrich
Visual
Partners

- Have one student in each pair write a decimal number (less than 5) to the hundredths place, while the other student writes a decimal number (less than 5) to the tenths place.
- Have partners find the sums of their decimals and then find the difference of their decimals using quick pictures.

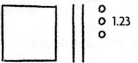

- Have partners subtract their sum from 10.55 and their difference from 5.5.

RtI Response to Intervention

Reteach Tier 1
Visual / Kinesthetic
Whole Class / Small Group

Write the expression 0.54 − 0.21 on the board.

- Ask students to discuss how they would solve the problem.
- Have students discuss how they could use what they know about the relationship between decimals and fractions to solve the problem.
  Students' responses should include an explanation that tenths and hundredths can be represented with fractions and decimals. 0.54 − 0.21 can be written as $\frac{54}{100} - \frac{21}{100}$.
- **Explain how you can solve the problem using fractions.** Possible answer: I can write the decimals as fractions and subtract: $\frac{54}{100} - \frac{21}{100} = \frac{33}{100}$. Then I can rewrite the difference as a decimal; $\frac{33}{100} = 0.33$.
- Have students use this method to find 2.3 − 1.5.
  $2\frac{3}{10} - 1\frac{5}{10} = \frac{8}{10} = 0.8$

Tier 2
Visual / Kinesthetic
Small Group

Materials color pencils, Decimal Models
(see *eTeacher Resources*)

- On the board, write 0.37 − 0.18. Remind students that in a hundredths decimal model, each square represents 1 hundredth and the entire square represents one.
- First model the greater number. **How many hundredths should you color?** 37 To represent subtraction, you can cross out hundredths. **How many hundredths should you cross out?** 18

- **Count the remaining hundredths and record the difference. What is 0.37 − 0.18?** 0.19
- Have students follow the same steps to find 0.59 − 0.25. 0.34

1 ENGAGE

Access Prior Knowledge On the board, write the subtraction problem shown below.

$$\begin{array}{r} 500 \\ -\ 249 \\ \hline \end{array}$$

Have students explain and demonstrate the regroupings that must occur to complete the subtraction.

2 TEACH and TALK

▶ Investigate

Materials base-ten blocks

After students complete the activity, ask them to formulate generalizations that describe when and how to regroup during decimal subtraction. Possible answer: I need to regroup whenever the value of the digit being subtracted is greater than the value of the digit I am subtracting from; regroup 1 tenth as 10 hundredths and 1 one as 10 tenths.

▶ Draw Conclusions

H.O.T. Problem For Exercise 2, there are different ways to conclude that the difference of the numbers will be less than 1; invite a variety of explanations.

COMMON CORE
CC.5.NBT.7 Add, subtract, multiply, and divide decimals to hundredths, using concrete models or drawings and strategies based on place value, properties of operations, and/or the relationship between addition and subtraction; relate the strategy to a written method and explain the reasoning used.

Name _____

Lesson 3.6

Decimal Subtraction

Essential Question How can you use base-ten blocks to model decimal subtraction?

COMMON CORE STANDARD CC.5.NBT.7
Perform operations with multi-digit whole numbers and with decimals to hundredths.

CONNECT You can use base-ten blocks to help you find the difference between two decimals.

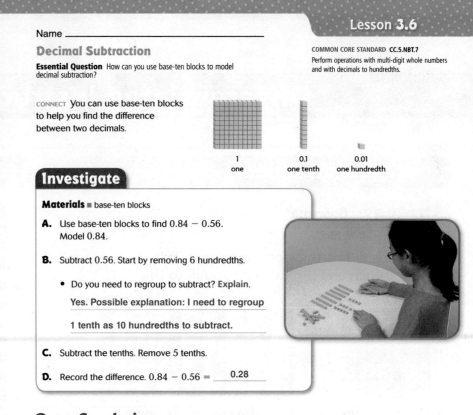

1	0.1	0.01
one	one tenth	one hundredth

Investigate

Materials ■ base-ten blocks

A. Use base-ten blocks to find $0.84 - 0.56$. Model 0.84.

B. Subtract 0.56. Start by removing 6 hundredths.

- Do you need to regroup to subtract? **Explain.**

  Yes. Possible explanation: I need to regroup

  1 tenth as 10 hundredths to subtract.

C. Subtract the tenths. Remove 5 tenths.

D. Record the difference. $0.84 - 0.56 = $ ___0.28___

Draw Conclusions

1. What if you remove the tenths first and then the hundredths? **Explain** how you would regroup.

   Possible explanation: I would still regroup by exchanging 1 tenth for

   10 hundredths.

2. **H.O.T. Synthesize** If two decimals are both less than 1.0, what do you know about the difference between them? **Explain.**

   Possible explanation: Since $0.99 - 0.01 = 0.98$ and is the greatest possible difference, I

   know that if both decimals are less than 1.0, the difference will also be less than 1.0.

Chapter 3 **125**

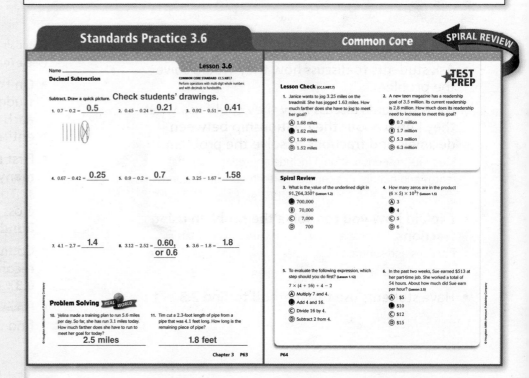

Standards Practice 3.6

Common Core SPIRAL REVIEW

Name _____

Decimal Subtraction

Lesson 3.6

COMMON CORE STANDARD CC.5.NBT.7
Perform operations with multi-digit whole numbers and with decimals to hundredths.

Subtract. Draw a quick picture. Check students' drawings.

1. $0.7 - 0.2 = $ ___0.5___   2. $0.45 - 0.24 = $ ___0.21___   3. $0.92 - 0.51 = $ ___0.41___

4. $0.67 - 0.42 = $ ___0.25___   5. $0.9 - 0.2 = $ ___0.7___   6. $3.25 - 1.67 = $ ___1.58___

7. $4.1 - 2.7 = $ ___1.4___   8. $3.12 - 2.52 = $ ___0.60, or 0.6___   9. $3.6 - 1.8 = $ ___1.8___

Problem Solving REAL WORLD

10. Yelina made a training plan to run 5.6 miles per day. So far, she has run 3.1 miles today. How much farther does she have to run to meet her goal for today?

    ___2.5 miles___

11. Tim cut a 2.3-foot length of pipe from a pipe that was 4.1 feet long. How long is the remaining piece of pipe?

    ___1.8 feet___

Chapter 3   **P63**

Lesson Check (CC.5.NBT.7)

1. Janice wants to jog 3.25 miles on the treadmill. She has jogged 1.63 miles. How much farther does she have to jog to meet her goal?
   - (A) 1.68 miles
   - (B) 1.62 miles
   - (C) 1.58 miles
   - (D) 1.52 miles

2. A new teen magazine has a readership goal of 3.5 million. Its current readership is 2.8 million. How much does its readership need to increase to meet this goal?
   - (A) 0.7 million
   - (B) 1.7 million
   - (C) 5.3 million
   - (D) 6.3 million

Spiral Review

3. What is the value of the underlined digit in 91,764,350? (Lesson 1.2)
   - (A) 700,000
   - (B) 70,000
   - (C) 7,000
   - (D) 700

4. How many zeros are in the product $(6 \times 5) \times 10^3$? (Lesson 1.5)
   - (A) 3
   - (B) 4
   - (C) 5
   - (D) 6

5. To evaluate the following expression, which step should you do first? (Lesson 1.12)

   $7 \times (4 + 16) \div 4 - 2$
   - (A) Multiply 7 and 4.
   - (B) Add 4 and 16.
   - (C) Divide 16 by 4.
   - (D) Subtract 2 from 4.

6. In the past two weeks, Sue earned $513 at her part-time job. She worked a total of 54 hours. About how much did Sue earn per hour? (Lesson 2.5)
   - (A) $5
   - (B) $10
   - (C) $12
   - (D) $15

P64

★ **TEST PREP**

Make Connections

You can use quick pictures to subtract decimals that need to be regrouped.

STEP 1

- Use a quick picture to model 2.82 − 1.47.

- Subtract the hundredths.

- Are there enough hundredths to remove? ___no___
  If there are not enough hundredths, regroup.

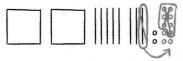

STEP 2

- Subtract the tenths.

- Are there enough tenths to remove? __yes__
  If there are not enough tenths, regroup.

- Subtract the ones.

STEP 3

Draw a quick picture of your answer. Then record.

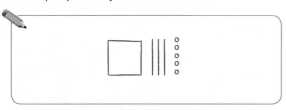

2.82 − 1.47 = ___1.35___

Possible explanation: I had to regroup in Step 1 because I did not have enough hundredths to remove 7 hundredths.

Math Talk MATHEMATICAL PRACTICES Explain why you have to regroup in Step 1.

126

▶ **Make Connections**

Step 1 Ask students to describe the regrouping needed to subtract the hundredths. One tenth was regrouped as 10 hundredths.

Step 2 Ask students to explain why there is no need to regroup to subtract the tenths. There are enough tenths to subtract.

Step 3 Ask students to tell what place value each part of their picture represents. The squares represents ones, the sticks represent tenths, and the circles represent hundredths.

Use **Math Talk** to focus on students' understanding of regrouping in decimal subtraction.

Make sure students understand that they have to regroup because there aren't enough hundredths to subtract 7 hundredths from 2 hundredths.

After the steps of the activity have been completed, challenge students to discuss, and then state, a general rule that describes where to place the decimal point in *any* answer that is found by subtracting two decimal numbers.

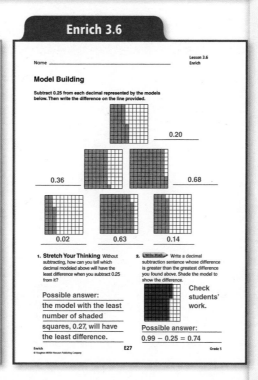

Reteach 3.6

Name _____   Lesson 3.6 Reteach

Decimal Subtraction

You can use decimal models to help you subtract decimals.

Subtract. 1.85 − 0.65

Step 1 Shade squares to represent 1.85.

Remember: By circling and crossing out shaded squares, you can see how many squares are taken away, or subtracted.

Step 2 Circle and cross out 65 of the shaded squares to represent subtracting 0.65.

Step 3 Count the shaded squares that are not crossed out. Altogether, 1 whole square and 20 one-hundredths squares, or 1.20 wholes, are NOT crossed out.
So, 1.85 − 0.65 = __1.20__

Subtract. Use decimal models. Draw a picture to show your work. Check students' drawings.

1. 1.4 − 0.61   2. 1.6 − 1.08

   __0.79__   __0.52__

3. 0.84 − 0.17   4. 1.39 − 1.14

   __0.67__   __0.25__

Reteach   R27   Grade 5
© Houghton Mifflin Harcourt Publishing Company

Enrich 3.6

Name _____   Lesson 3.6 Enrich

Model Building

Subtract 0.25 from each decimal represented by the models below. Then write the difference on the line provided.

0.20

0.36   0.68

0.02   0.63   0.14

1. **Stretch Your Thinking** Without subtracting, how can you tell which decimal modeled above will have the least difference when you subtract 0.25 from it?

Possible answer: the model with the least number of shaded squares, 0.27, will have the least difference.

2. **Write Math** Write a decimal subtraction sentence whose difference is greater than the greatest difference you found above. Shade the model to show your work.

Check students' work.

Possible answer:
0.99 − 0.25 = 0.74

Enrich   E27   Grade 5
© Houghton Mifflin Harcourt Publishing Company

⚠ COMMON ERRORS

Error When finding the difference, students place the decimal point incorrectly.

Example After Step 3, students write 13.5 or 0.135 for the answer.

Springboard to Learning A quick picture for the subtraction involves drawing a square, sticks, and circles. Remind students to write a decimal point after drawing the square and before drawing the sticks and circles.

PRACTICE Math Board

▶ **Share and Show** • **Guided Practice**

The first problem connects to the learning model. Have students use the MathBoard to explain their thinking.

Use Math Talk to focus on students' understanding of using quick pictures to model decimal subtraction. Make sure the explanations include the idea that you have to regroup one tenth as 10 hundredths when there aren't enough hundredths to subtract.

✔ **Quick Check**

If ➤ a student misses Exercises 6 and 7

Then ➤ **Differentiate Instruction with**
• RtI Tier 1 Activity, p. 125B
• Reteach 3.6

Go Deeper MATHEMATICAL PRACTICES

Write 4.15 − 2.79 on the board. **How will you know the number of regroupings that will be needed to find this answer?** Possible answer: since 9 hundredths is greater than 5 hundredths and 7 tenths is greater than 1 tenth, two regroupings will be needed.

Name _____

Share and Show ....

Complete the quick picture to find the difference.

1. 0.62 − 0.18 = ____0.44____

Subtract. Draw a quick picture. For 2–7, check students' drawings.

2. 3.41 − 1.74 = ____1.67____

3. 0.84 − 0.57 = ____0.27____

4. 0.93 − 0.38 = ____0.55____

5. 2.71 − 1.34 = ____1.37____

6. 4.05 − 1.61 = ____2.44____

7. 1.37 − 0.52 = ____0.85____

Math Talk MATHEMATICAL PRACTICES
Explain how you can use a quick picture to find 0.81 − 0.46.

Possible explanation: I can draw 0.81 using 8 lines for tenths and 1 small circle for hundredths. I would regroup 1 tenth as 10 hundredths. Then, I would subtract 6 hundredths from 11 hundredths. Last, I would subtract 4 tenths from the remaining 7 tenths. My answer is 0.35.

© Houghton Mifflin Harcourt Publishing Company

Chapter 3 • Lesson 6 127

Problem Solving . . . .

H.O.T. **Pose a Problem**

8. Antonio left his MathBoard on his desk during lunch. The quick picture below shows the problem he was working on when he left.

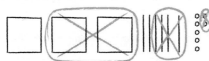

Write a problem that can be solved using the quick picture above.

Pose a problem.	Solve your problem.
Possible problem: Shana had 3.67 decimeters of string. She cut off 2.42 decimeters. How much string did Shana have left?	Possible solution: 3.67 − 2.42 = 1.25 decimeters

• Describe how you can change the problem by changing the quick picture.

Possible problem: I can change the quick picture by subtracting 1.73. The picture

will change because I will need to regroup 1 one as 10 tenths before subtracting.

3.67 − 1.73 = 1.94

FOR MORE PRACTICE:
Standards Practice Book, pp. P63–P64

▶ **Problem Solving**

H.O.T. Problem In Exercise 8, before students can pose and solve a problem, they must understand what the quick picture represents.

• **What decimal number does the black portion of the quick picture represent? Explain your answer.** 3.67; each square represents 1 one, each stick represents 1 tenth, and each circle represents 1 hundredth, so 3 + 0.6 + 0.07 = 3.67.

• **What does the portion marked with gray ovals and *X*s represent? Explain your answer** 2.42; The gray ovals and *X*s represent the decimal value that is subtracted.

4 SUMMARIZE

Essential Question

How can you use base-ten blocks to model decimal subtraction? Possible answer: Model the first number using flats, longs, and small cubes. Then model the number being subtracted by removing small cubes, longs, and then flats that represent the number. Regroup as needed.

Math Journal

Describe a problem involving decimals that you would use a quick picture to solve. Then solve the problem.

 INDEPENDENT ACTIVITIES

Differentiated Centers Kit

Literature
Halfpipe

Students read about adding and subtracting decimals to rank snowboarders in a competition.

Games
Ride the Course

Students add or subtract decimals to move ahead on the course.

Digital Path

- ☑ Animated Math Models
- *i*T *i*Tools
- ᛘᛘ HMH Mega Math
- ⭐ Soar to Success Math
- 🅶🅾 *e*Student Edition

Formative Assessment

Use the **Mid-Chapter Checkpoint** to assess students' learning and progress in the first half of the chapter. The formative assessment provides the opportunity to adjust teaching methods for individual or whole class instruction.

Name _____

✔ Mid-Chapter Checkpoint

▶ **Concepts and Skills**

1. **Explain** how you can use base-ten blocks to find $1.54 + 2.37$. (CC.5.NBT.7)

   Possible explanation: I can model 1.54 and 2.37. When I add the hundredths, I need to regroup 10 hundredths as 1 tenth. I add the 1 tenth to the 8 tenths to make 9 tenths. Then I add the ones, $1 + 2 = 3$. So the answer is 3.91.

Complete the sentence. (CC.5.NBT.1)

2. 0.04 is $\frac{1}{10}$ of ___0.4___.

3. 0.06 is 10 times as much as ___0.006___.

Write the value of the underlined digit. (CC.5.NBT.3a)

4. 6.5<u>4</u>
   four hundredths, or 0.04

5. 0.<u>8</u>37
   eight tenths, or 0.8

6. 8.70<u>2</u>
   two thousandths, or 0.002

7. <u>9</u>.173
   nine ones, or 9

Compare. Write <, >, or =. (CC.5.NBT.3b)

8. 6.52 ⟨=⟩ 6.520

9. 3.589 ⟨<⟩ 3.598

10. 8.463 ⟨<⟩ 8.483

Write the place value of the underlined digit. Round each number to the place of the underlined digit. (CC.5.NBT.4)

11. 0.<u>7</u>24
    tenths
    0.7

12. <u>2</u>.576
    ones
    3

13. 4.7<u>6</u>9
    hundredths
    4.77

Draw a quick picture to find the sum or difference. (CC.5.NBT.7)

14. $2.46 + 0.78 =$ ___3.24___

15. $3.27 - 1.84 =$ ___1.43___

© Houghton Mifflin Harcourt Publishing Company

Chapter 3 129

✔ Data-Driven Decision Making

Based on the results of the Mid-Chapter Checkpoint, use the following resources to strengthen individual or whole class instruction.

Item	Lesson	*CCSS	Common Error	Intervene With	Soar to Success Math
1	3.5	CC.5.NBT.7	May not regroup hundredths into tenths	R—3.5; TE—p. 121B	
2, 3	3.1	CC.5.NBT.1	May move the decimal point in the wrong direction	R—3.1; TE—p. 105B	4.27
4–7	3.2	CC.5.NBT.3a	May confuse place-value positions	R—3.2; TE—p. 109B	4.27
8–10	3.3	CC.5.NBT.3b	May not compare all place-value positions	R—3.3; TE—p. 113B	8.44
11–13	3.4	CC.5.NBT.4	May identify the wrong place-value position	R—3.4; TE—p. 117B	25.23
14, 15	3.5, 3.6	CC.5.NBT.7	May not regroup hundredths into tenths	R—3.5, 3.6; TE—pp. 121B, 125B	

*CCSS—Common Core State Standards   **Key: R**—Reteach Book; **TE**—RtI Activities

Fill in the bubble completely to show your answer.

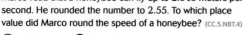

16. Marco read that a honeybee can fly up to 2.548 meters per second. He rounded the number to 2.55. To which place value did Marco round the speed of a honeybee? (CC.5.NBT.4)

Ⓐ ones   ● hundredths
Ⓑ tenths   Ⓓ thousandths

17. What is the relationship between 0.04 and 0.004? (CC.5.NBT.1)

● 0.04 is 10 times as much as 0.004
Ⓑ 0.04 is $\frac{1}{10}$ of 0.004
Ⓒ 0.004 is 10 times as much as 0.04
Ⓓ 0.04 is equal to 0.004

18. Jodi drew a quick picture to model the answer for 3.14 − 1.75. Which picture did she draw? (CC.5.NBT.7)

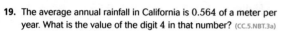

19. The average annual rainfall in California is 0.564 of a meter per year. What is the value of the digit 4 in that number? (CC.5.NBT.3a)

Ⓐ 4×1 Ⓒ $4 \times \frac{1}{100}$
Ⓑ $4 \times \frac{1}{10}$ ● $4 \times \frac{1}{1,000}$

20. Jan ran 1.256 miles on Monday, 1.265 miles on Wednesday, and 1.268 miles on Friday. What were her distances from greatest to least? (CC.5.NBT.3b)

Ⓐ 1.268 miles, 1.256 miles, 1.265 miles
● 1.268 miles, 1.265 miles, 1.256 miles
Ⓒ 1.265 miles, 1.256 miles, 1.268 miles
Ⓓ 1.256 miles, 1.265 miles, 1.268 miles

130

© Houghton Mifflin Harcourt Publishing Company

✓ Data-Driven Decision Making

Item	Lesson	*CCSS	Common Error	Intervene With	Soar to Success Math
16	3.4	CC.5.NBT.4	May identify the place-value position incorrectly	R—3.4; TE—p. 117B	25.23
17	3.1	CC.5.NBT.1	May divide instead of multiplying when moving to a decimal place on the right	R—3.1; TE—p. 105B	4.27
18	3.6	CC.5.NBT.7	May not regroup hundredths and tenths	R—3.6; TE—p. 125B	
19	3.2	CC.5.NBT.3a	May identify the wrong place-value position	R—3.2; TE—p. 109B	4.27
20	3.3	CC.5.NBT.3b	May not compare all place-value positions	R—3.3; TE—p. 113B	8.44

*CCSS—Common Core State Standards   **Key: R—Reteach Book; TE—RtI Activities**

Estimate Decimal Sums and Differences

LESSON AT A GLANCE

Common Core Standard
Perform operations with multi-digit whole numbers and with decimals to hundredths.
CC.5.NBT.7 Add, subtract, multiply, and divide decimals to hundredths, using concrete models or drawings and strategies based on place value, properties of operations, and/or the relationship between addition and subtraction; relate the strategy to a written method and explain the reasoning used.

Lesson Objective
Make reasonable estimates of decimal sums and differences.

Essential Question
How can you estimate decimal sums and differences?

Materials MathBoard

Digital Path

☑ Animated Math Models   GO MATH! eStudent Edition

PROFESSIONAL DEVELOPMENT
COMMON CORE

About the Math

Teaching for Depth In this lesson, students are introduced to using benchmarks to estimate. As you discuss this concept, point out that a great deal of latitude exists when choosing benchmarks. Some benchmarks, however, produce better estimates than others.

For example, if students are asked to use benchmarks to estimate the sum of several numbers in hundredths that are greater than 1 and less than 10, some students may choose to use a close whole number benchmark, while others may choose a close benchmark decimal (0.25, 0.5, 0.75). Generally speaking, the student who chooses a benchmark decimal will produce a more reasonable estimate of the exact sum. However, both students are using benchmarks correctly.

PODCASTING
Professional Development Video Podcasts

Daily Routines
Math Board

SPIRAL REVIEW
Common Core

Problem of the Day

eTransparency 3.7

Test Prep Marice received three pet finches. During a recent visit to the veterinarian's office, each bird's weight was recorded.

Weights of Finches	
Name of Finch	**Weight (in ounces)**
Leslie	0.59
Nellie	0.63
Mac	0.69

What is Mac's weight to the nearest tenth of an ounce?

Ⓐ 0.5 ounce   ● 0.7 ounce

Ⓑ 0.6 ounce   Ⓓ 1.0 ounce

Vocabulary Builder
Divide Using Word Form

Write the following problems on the board. Have students write the quotient for each exercise in standard form.

1. two hundred twenty divided by twenty-two 10

2. eight hundred thirty-seven divided by nine 93

3. one thousand, fifty-two divided by four 263

4. five thousand, six hundred thirty-one divided by three 1,877

Differentiated Instruction Activities

Language Support
Visual / Auditory | Small Group

Strategy: Model Language

- Students learn meaning by repeating modeled sentences.
- Show a number line with benchmarks for decimals.

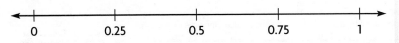

0	0.25	0.5	0.75	1

- Explain that these numbers are *benchmarks*.
- Show 0.23 on the number line. **The closest benchmark to 0.23 is 0.25.** Have students repeat the sentence.
- Identify benchmarks for other decimals. Have students repeat each sentence.

See Activity Guide for leveled activities.

Enrich
Visual | Small Group

- Have students make a menu for an imaginary café they may wish to open. Invite students to be creative about what items they might include on the menu. They should consider the prices that they have paid for various items.

Cook's Café	
Menu	**Prices**
Tuna Sandwich	$5.95
Pizza Slice	$2.95
Veggie Bites	$2.95
Drinks	$1.95

- Have them write the price of each item on the menu in dollars and cents.
- Have them list a combination of items from the menu that they could buy for $5, $10, and $20.
- To extend the activity, have students make "meals" out of the items that will cost less than buying the items individually.

RtI Response to Intervention

Reteach Tier 1
Visual / Kinesthetic | Whole Class / Small Group

- Students may incorrectly round each addend to a different place when estimating a sum or difference.

Have students consider 47.94 − 22.8.

- Identify the decimal with fewer decimal places. 22.8
- **Determine the place to which the decimal can be rounded.** Possible answer: 22.8 can be rounded to the ones place using the digit 8 in the tenths place.
- Round each decimal to that place. 48 and 23
- Subtract the estimates: **48 − 23.** 25

Have students apply these steps to other subtraction problems.

Tier 2
Visual / Kinesthetic | Small Group

Materials Number Lines (see *eTeacher Resources*)

- **Estimate 2.6 + 1.2.** Have students write the problem in vertical form on their papers as you write it on the board.
- Allow students time to graph each addend on a tenths number line. **Is 2.6 closer to 2 or 3?** 3 Have students record a 3 to the right of 2.6.
- **Is 1.2 closer to 1 or 2?** 1 Have students record a 1 to the right of 1.2. Add the whole numbers. On the board, write 2.6 + 1.2 *is about____*. Have students complete the sentence.

$$\begin{array}{cc} 2.6 & 3 \\ +\,1.2 & +\,1 \\ \hline & 4 \end{array}$$
2.6 + 1.2 is about 4.

- Have students estimate **0.8 + 2.1.** about 3

1 ENGAGE

Access Prior Knowledge

- Tell students that music is often stored on a CD. Have students research what is a reasonable estimate for how much music a CD can hold. Accept all reasonable answers. Although the answer depends in part on the compression rate, it is common for an audio CD to hold more than an hour of music and an MP3 CD to hold more than 200 songs.

2 TEACH and TALK Animated Math Models

▶ Unlock the Problem MATHEMATICAL PRACTICES

A word in this problem suggests that you should estimate instead of finding an exact answer. Read the problem to discover the word. The word "about" suggests an estimate.

Have students relate how they round a decimal to how they would round a whole number. They should conclude that rounding either decimals or whole numbers involves place value. Then have students estimate the sum of the three decimals by rounding each number to the nearest whole number.

Try This!

Have students estimate the difference for A and B at the bottom of the page. Students can round to the nearest dollar: $27.95 to $28 and $11.72 to $12 and subtract, or round to the nearest ten dollars: $27.95 to $30 and $11.72 to $10 and subtract.

- **What real-world situation can be modeled by the subtraction $27.95 − $11.72?** Possible answer: $27.95 and $11.72 represent the cost of two books. Subtract $11.72 from $27.95 to find how much more one book costs than the other book.

CC.5.NBT.7 Add, subtract, multiply, and divide decimals to hundredths, using concrete models or drawings and strategies based on place value, properties of operations, and/or the relationship between addition and subtraction; relate the strategy to a written method and explain the reasoning used.

Name _____

Lesson 3.7

Estimate Decimal Sums and Differences

Essential Question How can you estimate decimal sums and differences?

COMMON CORE STANDARD CC.5.NBT.7
Perform operations with multi-digit whole numbers and with decimals to hundredths.

🔓 UNLOCK the Problem REAL WORLD

A singer is recording a CD. The lengths of the three songs are 3.4 minutes, 2.78 minutes, and 4.19 minutes. About how much recording time will be on the CD?

🔑 **Use rounding to estimate.**

Round to the nearest whole number. Then add.

3.4	3
2.78	3
+ 4.19	+ 4
	10

Remember

To round a number, determine the place to which you want to round.

- If the digit to the right is less than 5, the digit in the rounding place stays the same.
- If the digit to the right is 5 or greater, the digit in the rounding place increases by 1.

So, there will be about __10__ minutes of recording time on the CD.

Try This! Use rounding to estimate.

Ⓐ Round to the nearest whole dollar. Then subtract.

$27.95	$28
− $11.72	− $12
	$16

To the nearest dollar, $27.95 − $11.72 is about __$16__.

Ⓑ Round to the nearest ten dollars. Then subtract.

$27.95	$30
− $11.72	− $10
	$20

To the nearest ten dollars, $27.95 − $11.72 is about __$20__.

- Do you want an overestimate or an underestimate when you estimate the total cost of items you want to buy? Explain.

  Possible explanation: I would want an overestimate to make sure I had enough money

  to buy the items.

© Houghton Mifflin Harcourt Publishing Company

Chapter 3   131

Standards Practice 3.7

Common Core SPIRAL REVIEW

Name _____

Estimate Decimal Sums and Differences

COMMON CORE STANDARD CC.5.NBT.7
Perform operations with multi-digit whole numbers and with decimals to hundredths.

Use rounding to estimate. Possible estimates are given.

1. 5.38 +6.14	2. 2.57 +0.14	3. 9.65 −3.12	4. 7.92 +5.37

5 +6
11

3   **7**   **13**

Use benchmarks to estimate. Possible estimates are given.

5. 2.81 +3.72	6. 12.54 + 7.98	7. 6.34 +3.95	8. 16.18 − 5.94

6.5   **20.5**   **10.25**   **10.25**

9. 17.09 + 3.98	10. 14.01 − 4.51	11. 11.47 + 9.02	12. 19.97 −11.02

21   **9.5**   **20.5**   **9**

Problem Solving REAL WORLD

Possible estimates are given.

13. Elian bought 1.87 pounds of chicken and 2.46 pounds of turkey at the deli. About how much meat did he buy altogether?

about 4.5 pounds

14. Jenna bought a gallon of milk at the store for $3.58. About how much change did she receive from a $20 bill?

$16.50

Chapter 3   P65

Lesson Check (CC.5.NBT.7)

1. Regina has two electronic files. One has a size of 3.15 MB and the other has a size of 4.89 MB. Which is the best estimate of the total size of the two electronic files?

Ⓐ 7 MB
Ⓑ 7.5 MB
● 8 MB
Ⓓ 8.5 MB

2. Madison is training for a marathon, which is 26.2 miles. She currently can run 18.5 miles in a day. About how many more miles in a day does she have to add to run the length of a marathon?

Ⓐ 8 miles
Ⓑ 7.5 miles
Ⓒ 6.5 miles
Ⓓ 6 miles

Spiral Review (CC.5.NBT.1, CC.5.NBT.3b, CC.5.NBT.4, CC.5.NBT.6)

3. A machine prints 8 banners in 120 seconds. How many seconds does it take to print one banner? (Lesson 2.2)

Ⓐ 10 seconds
Ⓑ 12 seconds
● 15 seconds
Ⓓ 18 seconds

4. To which place value is the number rounded? (Lesson 3.4)

5.319 to 5.3

Ⓐ ones
● tenths
Ⓒ hundredths
Ⓓ thousandths

5. The average distance from Mars to the sun is about one hundred forty-one million, six hundred twenty thousand miles. How do you write the number that shows this distance in standard form? (Lesson 1.2)

Ⓐ 141,620
Ⓑ 1,416,200
Ⓒ 14,162,000
● 141,620,000

6. Logan ate 1.438 pounds of grapes. His brother Ralph ate 1.44 pounds of grapes. Which brother ate more grapes? (Lesson 3.3)

Ⓐ Logan
● Ralph
Ⓒ They ate the same amount of grapes.
Ⓓ There is not enough information to decide which brother ate more grapes.

P66

★TEST PREP

Use Benchmarks Benchmarks are familiar numbers used as points of reference. You can use the benchmarks 0, 0.25, 0.50, 0.75, and 1 to estimate decimal sums and differences.

🔒 Example 1 Use benchmarks to estimate. 0.18 + 0.43

Locate and graph a point on the number line for each decimal. Identify which benchmark each decimal is closer to.

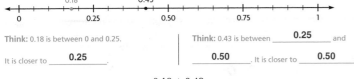

Think: 0.18 is between 0 and 0.25.

It is closer to ___0.25___.

Think: 0.43 is between ___0.25___ and ___0.50___. It is closer to ___0.50___.

$$\begin{array}{ccc} 0.18 & + & 0.43 \\ \downarrow & & \downarrow \\ 0.25 & + & 0.50 = 0.75 \end{array}$$

So, 0.18 + 0.43 is about ___0.75___.

🔒 Example 2 Use benchmarks to estimate. 0.76 − 0.22

Locate and graph a point on the number line for each decimal. Identify which benchmark each decimal is closer to.

Think: 0.76 is between ___0.75___ and ___1___. It is closer to ___0.75___.

Think: 0.22 is between 0 and 0.25. It is closer to ___0.25___.

$$\begin{array}{ccc} 0.76 & - & 0.22 \\ \downarrow & & \downarrow \\ 0.75 & - & 0.25 = 0.50 \end{array}$$

So, 0.76 − 0.22 is about ___0.50___.

Possible explanation: If I use rounding to estimate, 0.76 − 0.22 will be about 0.6. If I use benchmark decimals, it will be about 0.50.

Math Talk MATHEMATICAL PRACTICES
Use Example 2 to explain how using rounding or benchmarks to estimate a decimal difference can give you different answers.

© Houghton Mifflin Harcourt Publishing Company

132

Use Benchmarks

Before discussing the decimal benchmarks, help students connect them to equivalent fractions.

- **What fractions in simplest form are equivalent to the benchmarks 0.25, 0.5, and 0.75?** $0.25 = \frac{1}{4}$; $0.5 = \frac{1}{2}$; $0.75 = \frac{3}{4}$

▶ Example 1

Point out that it may be helpful to think of whole numbers when graphing points for decimal numbers.

- **Think about the whole numbers 0, 18, and 25. Is 18 closer to 0 or closer to 25? Explain how you know.** closer to 25; Explanations will vary.

- **When you locate eighteen hundredths on the number line, why do you place it closer to twenty-five hundredths than to zero?** Possible answer: The distance from 18 hundredths to 25 hundredths is less than the distance from 18 hundredths to zero.

- **What benchmarks can you use when rounding the number 6.35?** Possible answer: Instead of 0, 0.25, 0.5, 0.75, and 1, I can use 6, 6.25, 6.5, 6.75, and 7.

▶ Example 2

Point out to students that they can use the number line and benchmarks to estimate the difference.

Use **Math Talk** to focus on students' understanding of how using rounding compares to using benchmarks to estimate.

Have students explain why using rounding and benchmarks can give different answers.

⚠ COMMON ERRORS

Error Students do not graph numbers in sensible locations when benchmarks have different number of decimal place values.

Example Students do not recognize 0.5 as 0.50.

Springboard to Learning Review how to find equivalent decimals, and then have students rewrite 0.5 so that all of the benchmarks are numbers in hundredths.

▲ RtI

Reteach 3.7

Lesson 3.7
Reteach

Name _____

Estimate Decimal Sums and Differences

You can use rounding to help you estimate sums and differences.

Use rounding to estimate 1.24 + 0.82 + 3.4.

Round to the nearest whole number. Then add.

$$\begin{array}{rcl} 1.24 & \rightarrow & 1 \\ 0.82 & \rightarrow & 1 \\ + 3.4 & \rightarrow & +3 \\ \hline & & 5 \end{array}$$

So, the sum is about ___5___.

Remember:
If the digit to the right of the place you are rounding to is:
- less than 5, the digit in the rounding place stays the same.
- greater than or equal to 5, the digit in the rounding place increases by 1.

Use benchmarks to estimate 8.78 − 0.30.

$$\begin{array}{rcl} 8.78 & \rightarrow & 8.75 \\ - 0.30 & \rightarrow & -0.25 \\ \hline & & 8.5 \end{array}$$

Think: 0.78 is between 0.75 and 1.
It is closer to 0.75.

Think: 0.30 is between 0.25 and 0.50.
It is closer to 0.25.

So, the difference is about ___8.5___.

Use rounding to estimate. Possible estimates are given.

| 1. 51.23 −28.4 **23** | 2. $29.38 +$42.75 **$72** | 3. 7.6 −2.15 **6** | 4. 0.74 +0.20 **1** | 5. 2.08 0.56 +0.41 **3** |

Use benchmarks to estimate.

| 6. 6.17 −3.5 **2.75** | 7. 1.73 1.4 +3.17 **6.5** | 8. 3.28 −0.86 **2.5** | 9. 15.27 +41.8 **57** | 10. $23.07 −$ 7.83 **$15.25** |

| 11. 0.427 + 0.711 **1.25** | 12. 61.05 − 18.63 **42.25** | 13. 40.51 + 30.39 **71** |

Reteach
© Houghton Mifflin Harcourt Publishing Company

R28

Grade 5

Enrich 3.7

Lesson 3.7
Enrich

Name _____

Driving Decimals

Round the number of miles driven each day to the nearest whole number. Write the estimated total for each person in the last column. Then use the data in the table to solve the problems.

Possible estimates are given.

Number of Miles Traveled				
Driver	Friday	Saturday	Sunday	Total Miles
Mrs. McEnery	14.57	36.92	17.9	70
Ms. Sanders	90.7	39.77	24.33	155
Mrs. Adams	44.63	21.16	39.1	105
Mr. Harrison	73.23	50.58	45.55	170
Mr. Volga	68.85	32.46	62.12	163

1. On Friday, about how many more miles did Ms. Sanders drive compared to Mr. Volga?
   22 miles

2. About how many total miles did Mr. Harrison drive than Mrs. Adams?
   65 miles

3. About how many more miles did the driver who traveled the greatest total distance drive than the driver who traveled the least total distance?
   100 miles

4. About how many miles did Mr. Volga drive on Saturday and Sunday?
   94 miles

5. What is the estimated difference between the driver who traveled the greatest distance in one day and the driver who traveled the least distance in one day?
   76 miles

6. Estimate the difference between the greatest daily distance Mr. Harrison traveled and the least daily distance Mr. Harrison traveled.
   27 miles

7. Estimate the total number of miles all five drivers traveled on Saturday.
   181 miles

8. Write and solve your own estimation problem using the data from the table.
   Possible answer: about how many more miles did Mr. Harrison drive on Saturday than on Sunday?; about 5 more miles

Enrich
© Houghton Mifflin Harcourt Publishing Company

E28

Grade 5

3 PRACTICE

▶ Share and Show • Guided Practice

The first problem connects to the learning model. Have students use the MathBoard to explain their thinking.

Use **Math Talk** to focus on students' understanding of how estimates relate to exact answers. Extend the discussion by having students name words and phrases that suggest an estimate.

✔ Quick Check

If ▶	a student misses Exercises 3 and 5

Then ▶	**Differentiate Instruction** with

- RtI Tier 1 Activity, p. 131B
- Reteach 3.7
- ✦ Soar to Success Math 21.36, 22.36

Go Deeper

The number line on page 132 displays benchmarks for decimals from 0 to 1. Exercises 5, 9, 10, and 11 involve benchmarks that are greater than 1. After students complete these exercises, invite volunteers to describe the benchmarks that were chosen and explain how they were used.

Name _____

Share and Show

Use rounding to estimate. Possible estimates are given.

1.
$$\begin{array}{r} 2.34 \quad 2 \\ 1.9 \quad 2 \\ + 5.23 \quad + 5 \\ \hline 9 \end{array}$$

2.
$$\begin{array}{r} 10.39 \quad 10 \\ - 4.28 \quad - 4 \\ \hline 6 \end{array}$$

✓ 3.
$$\begin{array}{r} \$19.75 \quad \$20 \\ + \$ 3.98 \quad + \$4 \\ \hline \$24 \end{array}$$

Use benchmarks to estimate. Possible estimates are given.

4.
$$\begin{array}{r} 0.34 \quad 0.25 \\ 0.1 \quad 0 \\ + 0.25 \quad + 0.25 \\ \hline 0.50 \end{array}$$

✓ 5.
$$\begin{array}{r} 10.39 \quad 10.50 \\ - 4.28 \quad - 4.25 \\ \hline 6.25 \end{array}$$

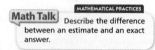 **Math Talk** Describe the difference between an estimate and an exact answer.

Possible explanation: An estimate is only an approximation of the sum or difference. An exact answer gives you the actual sum or difference.

On Your Own

Use rounding to estimate. Possible estimates are given.

6.
$$\begin{array}{r} 0.93 \quad 1 \\ + 0.18 \quad + 0 \\ \hline 1 \end{array}$$

7.
$$\begin{array}{r} 7.41 \quad 7 \\ - 3.88 \quad - 4 \\ \hline 3 \end{array}$$

8.
$$\begin{array}{r} 14.68 \quad 15 \\ - 9.93 \quad - 10 \\ \hline 5 \end{array}$$

Use benchmarks to estimate. Possible estimates are given.

9.
$$\begin{array}{r} 12.41 \quad 12.50 \\ - 6.47 \quad - 6.50 \\ \hline 6 \end{array}$$

10.
$$\begin{array}{r} 8.12 \quad 8.00 \\ + 5.52 \quad + 5.50 \\ \hline 13.50 \end{array}$$

11.
$$\begin{array}{r} 9.75 \quad 9.75 \\ - 3.47 \quad - 3.50 \\ \hline 6.25 \end{array}$$

Practice: Copy and Solve Use rounding or benchmarks to estimate. Possible estimates are given.

12. 12.83 + 16.24 29   13. $26.92 − $11.13 $16   14. 9.41 + 3.82 13

H.O.T. Estimate to compare. Write < or >. Possible estimates are given.

15. 2.74 + 4.22 ⊗ 3.13 + 1.87

7	5
estimate	estimate

16. 6.25 − 2.39 ⊗ 9.79 − 3.84

4	6
estimate	estimate

Math Talk in Action

Discuss how to use rounding to make an estimate.

Teacher: When you use rounding to estimate, how do you know which place to round to?

Jayden: Round to the greatest place.

Teacher: Look at Exercise 2. What is the greatest place in those numbers?

Abigail: Tens.

Teacher: To make an estimate for this exact answer, would you round to the nearest ten? Why or why not?

Ian: Yes. The greatest place is tens.

Natalie: The greatest place is tens, but if you round 4.28 to the nearest ten, it becomes zero. So your estimate would be 10 − 0 or 10. And that isn't a good estimate.

Carlos: A better estimate would be to round to the ones place.

Aaliyah: The numbers round to 10 and 4, so a good estimate is 6.

Teacher: Correct. When you estimate, rounding to the greatest place is a good idea when numbers have the same number of places. But sometimes we must choose a lesser place value.

Problem Solving REAL WORLD

For 17 and 20, possible estimates are given.

Use the table to solve 17–18. Show your work.

17. For the week of April 4, 1964, the Beatles had the top four songs. About how long would it take to listen to these four songs?

_____ **about 10 minutes**

Top Songs		
Number	Song Title	Song Length (in minutes)
1	"Can't Buy Me Love"	2.30
2	"She Loves You"	2.50
3	"I Want to Hold Your Hand"	2.75
4	"Please Please Me"	2.00

18. **What's the Error?** Isabelle says she can listen to the first three songs in the table in 6 minutes.

Possible answer: Each song is longer

than 2 minutes, so it would take Isabelle

longer than 6 minutes to listen to all

three songs.

19. ⭐ **Test Prep** Fran bought sneakers for $54.26 and a shirt for $34.34. If Fran started with $100, about how much money does she have left?

Ⓐ $5
🅑 $20
Ⓒ $35
Ⓓ $80

Connect to Science

Nutrition
Your body needs protein to build and repair cells. You should get a new supply of protein each day. The average 10-year-old needs 35 grams of protein daily. You can find protein in foods like meat, vegetables, and dairy products.

Grams of Protein per Serving	
Type of Food	Protein (in grams)
1 scrambled egg	6.75
1 cup shredded wheat cereal	5.56
1 oat bran muffin	3.99
1 cup low-fat milk	8.22

Use estimation to solve.

20. Gina had a scrambled egg, an oat bran muffin, and a cup of low-fat milk for breakfast. About how many grams of protein did Gina have at breakfast?

_____ **about 19 grams**

21. Pablo had a cup of shredded wheat cereal, a cup of low-fat milk, and one other item for breakfast. He had about 21 grams of protein. What was the third item Pablo had for breakfast?

_____ **a scrambled egg**

© Houghton Mifflin Harcourt Publishing Company

▶ ## Problem Solving

What's the Error? Ask students who give a general answer such as "Isabelle didn't round correctly." to detail the error that she made.

⭐ Test Prep Coach

In Exercise 19, if students selected:

A They did not round to an appropriate place.
C They used a rounded amount for the shirt.
D They did not correctly subtract the amount spent from the amount Fran started with.

▶ ## Connect to Science

After students read each problem, ask them if an estimate or an exact answer is needed, and have them give a reason to support their answer.

④ SUMMARIZE

Essential Question

How can you estimate decimal sums and differences? Possible answer: Rounding and number lines with benchmarks can be used to estimate decimal sums and differences.

Math Journal

Explain why estimation is an important skill to know when adding and subtracting decimals.

Differentiated Instruction
INDEPENDENT ACTIVITIES

Grab-and-Go!™
Differentiated Centers Kit

Activities
Get Around!

Students complete blue Activity Card 5 by adding decimals to find the perimeter of classroom objects.

Literature
Halfpipe

Students read about adding and subtracting decimals to rank snowboarders in a competition.

Games
Ride the Course

Students add or subtract decimals to move ahead on the course.

Digital Path

- 📺 Animated Math Models
- *i*T *i*Tools
- MM HMH Mega Math
- ⭐ Soar to Success Math
- GO eStudent Edition

Lesson 3.7   134

Add Decimals

LESSON AT A GLANCE

Common Core Standard

Perform operations with multi-digit whole numbers and with decimals to hundredths.

CC.5.NBT.7 Add, subtract, multiply, and divide decimals to hundredths, using concrete models or drawings and strategies based on place value, properties of operations, and/or the relationship between addition and subtraction; relate the strategy to a written method and explain the reasoning used.

Lesson Objective

Add decimals using place value.

Essential Question

How can place value help you add decimals?

Materials MathBoard

Digital Path

MM **HMH Mega Math**

GO **eStudent Edition**

COMMON CORE
PROFESSIONAL DEVELOPMENT

About the Math

Teaching for Depth When students complete the addition in this lesson, they learn how using place values helps when they add decimals. Prior knowledge of expanded notation can be used to demonstrate that aligning the decimal points of addends helps ensure that they add ones to ones, tenths to tenths, hundredths to hundredths, and so on.

$$
\begin{array}{llll}
3.1 & = 3 & + 0.1 & \\
0.45 & = 0 & + 0.4 & + 0.05 \\
+\ 6.21 & = 6 & + 0.2 & + 0.01 \\
\hline
& = 9 & + 0.7 & + 0.06 = 9.76
\end{array}
$$

PODCASTING **Professional Development Video Podcasts**

Daily Routines

Math Board

Common Core

SPIRAL REVIEW

Problem of the Day

eTransparency
3.8

Test Prep Mr. Miller purchased two coats that cost the same amount from an online store. The total amount Mr. Miller paid was $118. What was the price of one coat?

  Ⓐ $60   © $56

  ● $59   Ⓓ $55

Fluency Builder

Skills Practice Have students find the following sums.

1.	235 + 182 417	**2.**	2,040 + 1,376 3,416

3.   634
   + 380
   1,014

4.	320 + 137 457	**5.**	563 + 260 823

6.   786
   + 290
   1,076

7.	430 + 249 679	**8.**	995 + 47 1,042

9.   799
   + 834
   1,633

Literature

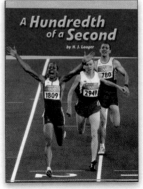

From the Grab-and-Go™ Differentiated Centers Kit

Students read about Olympic events in which competitors' times are just tenths or hundredths of a second apart.

A Hundredth of a Second

Differentiated Instruction Activities

ELL Language Support
 Visual / Small Group

Strategy: Model Concepts

Materials index cards, markers

- Students understand concepts and vocabulary when they are modeled or illustrated.

- Have students read and write decimal numbers on index cards.

- Choose two cards and have students show how to line up the decimals for addition. Then have students find the sum.

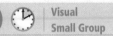

| 5.6 | 0.41 | 3.02 | 14.1 |
| 9.09 | 0.3 | 10.5 | 1.01 |

- Repeat with other pairs of cards.

See ELL Activity Guide for leveled activities.

Enrich
 Visual / Small Group

- Display the following chart:

Element	Atomic Weight
Lead	207.2
Gallium	69.72
Tin	118.71

- Have students write addition word problems using the data.

- For example: **What is the sum of the atomic weights of lead and tin?** 325.91

- Extend the activity by having students find the atomic weights of other elements and write word problems using the data.

RtI Response to Intervention

Reteach Tier 1
 Visual / Spatial Whole Class / Small Group

Materials grid paper

- Display 52.7 + 0.36 in vertical form.

- Have students work in small groups to place each digit in a column of the grid paper. Placing the decimal point first

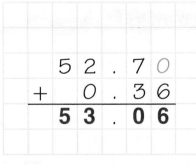

will help students keep the correct alignment. Then students use what they know about regrouping to write the sum.

- **How did the grid paper help you solve the problem?** Possible answer: By writing one number in each column, I was able to align the digits by place value.

Tier 2
Visual / Kinesthetic Small Group

Materials Place-Value Charts (see *eTeacher Resources*)

- Write 6.14 + 0.2 on the board. Give students place-value charts.

- **Write 6.14 in the chart. Then write 0.2 in the chart beneath 6.14. What do you notice about the second addend?** 0.2 does not have a digit in the hundredths place.

- Place a zero in the hundredths place of 0.2. **Did you change the value of 0.2 after writing a zero?** no

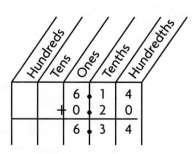

- Have students add the digits in each place, starting at the right. **What is 6.14 + 0.2?** 6.34

1 ENGAGE

Access Prior Knowledge

Point out that the average amount of rainfall a state receives each year may be described to the nearest inch or to the nearest centimeter.

- **To the nearest centimeter, what is your estimate of the average amount of rainfall your town or city receives each year?** Estimates will vary.

2 TEACH and TALK GO Online HMH Mega Math

▶ Unlock the Problem MATHEMATICAL PRACTICES

Rainfall is measured to a decimal place. Read the problem to discover to which decimal place the rainfall is measured. (In the problem, Henry measured the rainfall to hundredths of a centimeter.)

Discuss the quick pictures that students draw.

- **Do you have to regroup to complete the quick picture? Explain how you know.** Yes. There are 11 tenths (or sticks), and I must regroup when the value of a place is 10 or more.

- **Describe the regrouping using place-value names.** Eleven tenths are regrouped as 1 one and 1 tenth.

In the activity, have students note the alignment of the decimal points in the vertical addition.

Use Math Talk to focus on students' understanding of how to determine when regrouping is necessary.

COMMON CORE

CC.5.NBT.7 Add, subtract, multiply, and divide decimals to hundredths, using concrete models or drawings and strategies based on place value, properties of operations, and/or the relationship between addition and subtraction; relate the strategy to a written method and explain the reasoning used.

Name _____

Lesson **3.8**

Add Decimals

Essential Question How can place value help you add decimals?

COMMON CORE STANDARD CC.5.NBT.7
Perform operations with multi-digit whole numbers and with decimals to hundredths.

🔑 UNLOCK the Problem REAL WORLD

Henry recorded the amount of rain that fell over 2 hours. In the first hour, Henry measured 2.35 centimeters of rain. In the second hour, he measured 1.82 centimeters of rain.

Henry estimated that about 4 centimeters of rain fell in 2 hours. What is the total amount of rain that fell? How can you use this estimate to decide if your answer is reasonable?

Add. 2.35 + 1.82

- Add the hundredths first.

  5 hundredths + 2 hundredths = __7__ hundredths.

- Then add the tenths and ones. Regroup as needed.

  3 tenths + 8 tenths = __11__ tenths. Regroup.

  2 ones + 1 one + 1 regrouped one = __4__ ones.

$$\begin{array}{r} 1 \\ 2.35 \\ + 1.82 \\ \hline 4.17 \end{array}$$

- Record the sum for each place value.

Draw a quick picture to check your work.

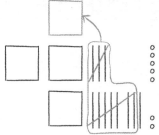

Math Talk MATHEMATICAL PRACTICES
Explain how you know when you need to regroup in a decimal addition problem.

Possible explanation: I know that I need to regroup when I have more than 9 hundredths or 9 tenths.

So, __4.17__ centimeters of rain fell.

Since __4.17__ is close to the estimate, 4, the answer is reasonable.

Chapter 3 **135**

Standards Practice 3.8

Common Core SPIRAL REVIEW

Name _____

Add Decimals Possible estimates are given.

Lesson **3.8**

COMMON CORE STANDARD CC.5.NBT.7
Perform operations with multi-digit whole numbers and with decimals to hundredths.

Estimate. Then find the sum.

1. Estimate: **10**
   $$\begin{array}{r} 2.85 \\ +7.29 \\ \hline \end{array}$$
   $$\begin{array}{r} 1\ 1 \\ 2.85 \\ +7.29 \\ \hline 10.14 \end{array}$$

2. Estimate: **11**
   $$\begin{array}{r} 4.23 \\ +6.51 \\ \hline \end{array}$$
   10.74

3. Estimate: **11**
   $$\begin{array}{r} 6.8 \\ +4.2 \\ \hline \end{array}$$
   11.0, or 11

4. Estimate: **8**
   $$\begin{array}{r} 2.7 \\ +5.37 \\ \hline \end{array}$$
   8.07

Find the sum.

5. 6.8 + 4.4
   11.2

6. 6.87 + 5.18
   12.05

7. 3.14 + 2.9
   6.04

8. 16.18 + 5.94
   22.12

9. 19.8 + 31.45
   51.25

10. 25.47 + 7.24
    32.71

11. 9.17 + 5.67
    14.84

12. 19.7 + 5.46
    25.16

Problem Solving REAL WORLD

13. Marcela's dog gained 4.1 kilograms in two months. Two months ago, the dog's mass was 5.6 kilograms. What is the dog's current mass?
    9.7 kilograms

14. During last week's storm, 2.15 inches of rain fell on Monday and 1.68 inches of rain fell on Tuesday. What was the total amount of rainfall on both days?
    3.83 inches

Chapter 3 **P67**

TEST PREP

Lesson Check (CC.5.NBT.7)

1. Lindsay has two packages she wants to mail. One package weighs 6.3 ounces, and the other package weighs 4.9 ounces. How much do the packages weigh together?
   - Ⓐ 11.4 ounces
   - ● 11.2 ounces
   - Ⓒ 10.9 ounces
   - Ⓓ 10.5 ounces

2. Anton rode his mountain bike three days in a row. He biked 12.1 miles on the first day, 13.4 miles on the second day, and 17.9 miles on the third day. How many total miles did Anton bike during the three days?
   - Ⓐ 58.2 miles
   - Ⓑ 47.1 miles
   - ● 43.4 miles
   - Ⓓ 42.4 miles

Spiral Review (CC.5.NBT.1, CC.5.NBT.2, CC.5.NBT.6)

3. In the number 2,145,857, how does the digit 5 in the thousands place compare to the digit 5 in the tens place? (Lesson 1.1)
   - Ⓐ It is 10 times greater.
   - ● It is 100 times greater.
   - Ⓒ It is 1,000 times greater.
   - Ⓓ It is 10,000 times greater.

4. Which of the following expressions does NOT have the same value as 10^5? (Lesson 1.4)
   - Ⓐ $10 \times 10 \times 10 \times 10 \times 10$
   - Ⓑ 100,000
   - ● the fifth power of 10
   - ● $5 \times 10,000$

5. Carmen works at a pet store. To feed 8 cats, she empties four 6-ounce cans of cat food into a large bowl. Carmen divides the food equally among the cats. How many ounces of food will each cat get? (Lesson 1.9)
   - ● 3 ounces
   - Ⓑ 4 ounces
   - Ⓒ 6 ounces
   - Ⓓ 8 ounces

6. There are 112 students in the Hammond Middle School marching band. The band director wants the students to march with 14 students in each row for the upcoming parade. How many rows will there be? (Lesson 2.3)
   - ● 8
   - Ⓑ 10
   - Ⓒ 12
   - Ⓓ 14

P68

Equivalent Decimals When adding decimals, you can use equivalent decimals to help keep the numbers aligned in each place. Add zeros to the right of the last digit as needed, so that the addends have the same number of decimal places.

Try This! Estimate. Then find the sum.

STEP 1	STEP 2
Estimate the sum. $20.4 + 13.76$ Estimate: $20 + 14 = \underline{34}$	**Find the sum.** Add the hundredths first. Then, add the tenths, ones, and tens. Regroup as needed. $\begin{array}{r} 1 \\ 2\,0.4\,0 \\ +\,1\,3.7\,6 \\ \hline 3\,4.1\,6 \end{array}$ Think: 20.4 = 20.40

$20.40 + 13.76 = \underline{34.16}$

- Is your answer reasonable? Explain.

  Yes; Possible explanation: because it is close to my estimate of 34

Share and Show

Estimate. Then find the sum.   Possible estimates are given.

1. Estimate: __8__
$\begin{array}{r} 2.5 \\ +\,4.6 \\ \hline 7.1 \end{array}$

2. Estimate: __15__
$\begin{array}{r} 8.75 \\ +\,6.43 \\ \hline 15.18 \end{array}$

☑ 3. Estimate: __10__
$\begin{array}{r} 2.03 \\ +\,7.89 \\ \hline 9.92 \end{array}$

4. Estimate: __10__

$6.34 + 3.8 = \underline{10.14}$

☑ 5. Estimate: __9__

$5.63 + 2.6 = \underline{8.23}$

Math Talk   MATHEMATICAL PRACTICES
Explain why it is important to remember to line up the place values in each number when adding or subtracting decimals.

Possible explanation: If I don't line up the place values correctly, I could add or subtract the wrong place values in the numbers.

Try This!

Have students estimate and find the sum.

Step 1 Ask students to describe how to estimate the sum. Round each addend to the nearest whole number and add to estimate the sum.

Step 2 Ask students to explain why you need to write a zero in the decimal addend before adding. I write a zero as needed so that both addends have the same place values.

❸ PRACTICE

▶ Share and Show • Guided Practice

The first problem connects to the learning model. Have students use the MathBoard to explain their thinking.

Use Exercises 3 and 5 for **Quick Check**. Students show their answers for the Quick Check on the Mathboard.

Use **Math Talk** to emphasize to students the importance of aligning decimals by place value before adding.

Quick Check

Then If a student misses Exercises 3 and 5

Differentiate Instruction with
- RtI Tier 1 Activity, p. 135B
- Reteach 3.8
- Soar to Success Math 21.37

⚠ **COMMON ERRORS**

Error Students do not align place values correctly.

Example For 20.4 + 13.76, students do not record two decimal places in the answer.

Springboard to Learning Have students shade one column of a grid and write only decimal points in it. Students can use a computational grid, grid paper, or lined paper turned sideways.

Reteach 3.8   ▲ RtI

Name _____   Lesson 3.8 Reteach

Add Decimals

Add. 4.37 + 9.8

Step 1 Estimate the sum.

$4.37 + 9.8$

Estimate: $4 + 10 = 14$

Step 2 Line up the place values for each number in a place-value chart. Then add.

	Ones	Tenths	Hundredths
	4	3	7
+	9	8	
	14	1	7	← sum

Step 3 Use your estimate to determine if your answer is reasonable.

Think: 14.17 is close to the estimate, 14. The answer is reasonable.

So, 4.37 + 9.8 = __14.17__

Estimate. Then find the sum. Possible estimates are given.

1. Estimate: __1__
$\begin{array}{r} 1.20 \\ +\,0.34 \\ \hline 1.54 \end{array}$

2. Estimate: __3__
$\begin{array}{r} 1.52 \\ +\,1.21 \\ \hline 2.73 \end{array}$

3. Estimate: __23__
$\begin{array}{r} 12.25 \\ +\,11.25 \\ \hline 23.50 \text{ or } 23.5 \end{array}$

4. Estimate: __12__
$\begin{array}{r} 10.75 \\ +\,1.11 \\ \hline 11.86 \end{array}$

5. Estimate: __41__
$\begin{array}{r} 22.65 \\ +\,18.01 \\ \hline 40.66 \end{array}$

6. Estimate: __49__
$\begin{array}{r} 34.41 \\ +\,15.37 \\ \hline 49.78 \end{array}$

Reteach   R29   Grade 5
© Houghton Mifflin Harcourt Publishing Company

Enrich 3.8

Name _____   Lesson 3.8 Enrich

Sum Match-Up

Find the sum of the decimals shown on each cube. Then match each sum to the square with the correct sum.

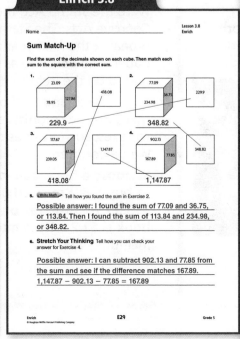

5. **Write Math** Tell how you found the sum in Exercise 2.

Possible answer: I found the sum of 77.09 and 36.75, or 113.84. Then I found the sum of 113.84 and 234.98, or 348.82.

6. **Stretch Your Thinking** Tell how you can check your answer for Exercise 4.

Possible answer: I can subtract 902.13 and 77.85 from the sum and see if the difference matches 167.89.

$1{,}147.87 - 902.13 - 77.85 = 167.89$

Enrich   E29   Grade 5
© Houghton Mifflin Harcourt Publishing Company

On Your Own • Independent Practice

Remind students to make an estimate before finding each sum, and then use the estimate to determine the reasonableness of the answer.

H.O.T. Problems Exercises 12–15 involve translating words to decimal numbers. For each exercise, ask:

- **Are the numbers described in this problem whole numbers or decimal numbers? Explain how you know.** Possible explanations: They are decimal numbers; the word "and" represents a decimal point.

After students complete the exercises on this page, give them an opportunity to compare and contrast adding whole numbers and decimal numbers.

- **How is adding decimal numbers like adding whole numbers?** Possible answer: To add both kinds of numbers, I align the place values, add, and regroup if necessary.

- **How is adding decimal numbers different from adding whole numbers?** Possible answer: The sum of decimal addends includes a decimal point; the sum of whole number addends does not.

Name _____

On Your Own ....

Estimate. Then find the sum. Possible estimates are given.

6. Estimate: __17__
$$\begin{array}{r} 12.3 \\ +\ 4.9 \\ \hline 17.2 \end{array}$$

7. Estimate: __32__
$$\begin{array}{r} 19.2 \\ +12.68 \\ \hline 31.88 \end{array}$$

8. Estimate: __14__
$$\begin{array}{r} 6.8 \\ +7.4 \\ \hline 14.2 \end{array}$$

9. Estimate: __11__

$7.86 + 2.9 =$ __10.76__

10. Estimate: __6__

$4.3 + 2.49 =$ __6.79__

11. Estimate: __10__

$9.95 + 0.47 =$ __10.42__

H.O.T. Find the sum.

12. seven and twenty-five hundredths added to nine and four tenths

__16.65__

13. twelve and eight hundredths added to four and thirty-five hundredths

__16.43__

14. nineteen and seven tenths added to four and ninety-two hundredths

__24.62__

15. one and eighty-two hundredths added to fifteen and eight tenths

__17.62__

Practice: Copy and Solve Find the sum.

16. $7.99 + 8.34$ 16.33

17. $15.76 + 8.2$ 23.96

18. $9.6 + 5.49$ 15.09

19. $33.5 + 16.4$ 49.9

20. $9.84 + 21.52$ 31.36

21. $3.89 + 4.6$ 8.49

22. $42.19 + 8.8$ 50.99

23. $16.74 + 5.34$ 22.08

24. $27.58 + 83.9$ 111.48

© Houghton Mifflin Harcourt Publishing Company

Cross-Curricular   **SCIENCE**

- Students experience precipitation in the form of rain, sleet, snow, and hail. Have them consider times of the year and locations they associate with each form. For example, students may relate summer in Florida to heavy rains.

- Baguio, Philippines receives an average of 180.04 inches of rain each year. Bogor, Indonesia receives an average of 166.33 inches of rain each year. What is the sum of the average rainfalls of the two cities each year? 346.37 inches each year

SOCIAL STUDIES

- Some of the events that led to the American Revolution were the Stamp Act, the Townshend Acts, and the Coercive Acts. The Stamp Act was passed in 1765 and repealed the next year. It taxed various items, such as paper, one pence to as much as 2 pounds. A stamp was placed on the item to show that the tax had been paid.

- Do research and find out how taxes on the colonists compare to taxes, such as sales tax, that we pay on items.

- **Suppose a book you want to buy has a marked price of $18.55, and the tax on that book is $1.21. How much would the book cost, including tax?** $19.76

UNLOCK the Problem   REAL WORLD

TEST PREP

25. A city receives an average rainfall of 16.99 centimeters in August. One year, during the month of August, it had rained 8.33 centimeters by August 15th. Then it rained another 4.65 centimeters through the end of the month. What was the total rainfall in centimeters for the month?

- (A) 3.68 centimeters
- (B) 4.68 centimeters
- (C) 12.98 centimeters
- (D) 13.98 centimeters

a. What do you need to find? how much rain fell altogether

b. What information are you given? the amount of rain from August 1 to August 15, and the amount of rain from August 16 to August 31

c. How will you use addition to find the total number of centimeters of rain that fell?

I will add the two amounts for the two time periods in August.

d. Show how you solved the problem.

```
  8.33
+ 4.65
 12.98
```

e. Fill in the bubble for the correct answer choice above.

26. Tania measured the growth of her plant each week. The first week, the plant's height measured 2.65 decimeters. During the second week, Tania's plant grew 0.38 decimeter. How tall was Tania's plant at the end of the second week?

- (A) 2.27 decimeters
- (B) 3.03 decimeters
- (C) 3.23 decimeters
- (D) 3.93 decimeters

27. Maggie had $35.13. Then her mom gave her $7.50 for watching her younger brother. How much money does Maggie have now?

- (A) $31.63
- (B) $32.63
- (C) $41.63
- (D) $42.63

138   **FOR MORE PRACTICE:**
Standards Practice Book, pp. P67–P68

© Houghton Mifflin Harcourt Publishing Company

▶ Unlock the Problem

Remind students of the importance of aligning place values before adding decimal numbers.

☆ Test Prep Coach

Test Prep Coach helps teachers identify common errors that students can make.

In Exercise 26, if students selected:

A They subtracted 0.38 from 2.65.
C They added the tenths place incorrectly.
D They regrouped 13 hundredths as 1 one and 3 hundredths.

④ SUMMARIZE

Essential Question

How can place value help you add decimals?
Possible answer: Aligning the place values of decimal addends helps me add hundredths to hundredths, tenths to tenths, ones to ones, and so on.

Math Journal

Describe an addition problem that you may need to regroup hundredths to solve.

Differentiated Instruction   INDEPENDENT ACTIVITIES

Grab-and-Go!
Differentiated Centers Kit

Activities
Add-A-Round

Students complete orange Activity Card 5 by finding decimal addends that equal a given sum.

Literature
A Hundredth of a Second

Students read about Olympic events in which competitors' times are just tenths or hundredths of a second apart.

Games
Ride the Course

Students add or subtract decimals to move ahead on the course.

Digital Path

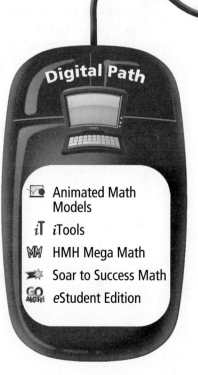

- 📺 Animated Math Models
- *iT* iTools
- 〽️ HMH Mega Math
- ☆ Soar to Success Math
- GO Math! eStudent Edition

Lesson 3.8   138

Subtract Decimals

LESSON AT A GLANCE

Common Core Standard
Perform operations with multi-digit whole numbers and with decimals to hundredths.
CC.5.NBT.7 Add, subtract, multiply, and divide decimals to hundredths, using concrete models or drawings and strategies based on place value, properties of operations, and/or the relationship between addition and subtraction; relate the strategy to a written method and explain the reasoning used.

Lesson Objective
Subtract decimals using place value.

Essential Question
How can place value help you subtract decimals?

Materials MathBoard

Digital Path

 Animated Math Models   eStudent Edition

PROFESSIONAL DEVELOPMENT
About the Math

Teaching for Depth Students know from their work with fractions that when the denominators of two or more fractions are the same, they simply add the numerators to find the sum of the fractions. Students also know that it is helpful to write equivalent decimals when the decimals in an addition or subtraction problem have a different number of decimal places.

Writing equivalent decimals and adding fractions with like denominators are related concepts.

$$2.3 \ = \ 2.30 = \ 2 + \frac{30}{100}$$
$$+\ 4.17 = +\ 4.17 = +\ 4 + \frac{17}{100}$$
$$\overline{6.47 \qquad\quad = \ 6 + \frac{47}{100} = 6\frac{47}{100}}$$

 Professional Development Video Podcasts

Daily Routines

Common Core

SPIRAL REVIEW

Problem of the Day

eTransparency **3.9**

Test Prep Charisse has two pieces of rope. One measures 1.15 feet and the other measures 0.8 foot. About how much total length of rope does Charisse have?

Ⓐ about 0.5 foot
Ⓑ about 1 foot
Ⓒ about 1.5 feet
Ⓓ about 2 feet

Fluency Builder

Skills Practice Have students find the following differences.

1.	336 − 228 108	**2.**	68 − 43 25	**3.**	1,320 − 804 516
4.	1,580 − 967 613	**5.**	1,605 − 150 1,455	**6.**	73 − 54 19
7.	2,140 − 1,697 443	**8.**	1,583 − 1,145 438	**9.**	1,274 − 1,054 220

Differentiated Instruction Activities

ELL Language Support
🕐 Verbal / Linguistic
Small Group

Strategy: Creative Grouping

Materials index cards, markers

- Group beginning and intermediate English Learners with advanced English Learners to help with language practice.

- Have students write decimal numbers on index cards.

| 5.6 | 0.41 | 3.02 | 14.1 |

| 9.09 | 0.3 | 10.5 | 1.01 |

- Have students choose two cards, write the numbers, and explain the steps to subtract the decimals.

- Make sure students explain how 0.3 is the same as 0.30.

See ELL Activity Guide for leveled activities.

Enrich
🕐 Logical
Small Group

Have students incorporate decimals and their understanding of equations to solve this problem:

- **Jane wants to know the mass of a pack of four bottles of juice. The materials she has to use include: six bottles of juice, 0.25 kg, 0.5 kg, 0.75 kg and 1 kg masses, and a pan balance. She finds that four bottles of juice balance two bottles of juice and one 0.75 kg mass. Can she solve the problem? What is the mass of four bottles of juice? Explain.** Possible explanation: She has the materials and information necessary to solve her problem. She can remove two bottles from both sides of the pan balance. So, two bottles on one side balance 0.75 kg on the other side. She can add two bottles back to one side and another 0.75 kg mass to the other. She then needs to add 0.75 kg + 0.75 kg to find the mass of the four bottles: 1.5 kg.

RtI Response to Intervention

Reteach Tier 1
🕐 Visual / Spatial
Whole Class / Small Group

Explain to students that a template is a guide or model that can be used in similar situations over and over.

- Have partners make a template for subtracting decimals. Ask: **What would be important to include on your template?** Possible answers: The decimal places are lined up; each number aligns with a number of the same place value.

- **How will you leave room for regrouping?** Possible answer: place smaller boxes above the digits in the top value.

- Have partners present their templates. You may wish to photocopy the templates and allow students to use them when working.

Tier 2
🕐 Visual / Kinesthetic
Small Group

Materials Place-Value Charts (see *eTeacher Resources*)

- On the board, draw the subtraction template shown below without numbers. Next to the template, write 5.2 − 3.6. Have students write each number in the template.

- **Start with the tenths. Can you subtract 6 tenths from 2 tenths?** no **You can regroup 1 one as 10 tenths. How do you record this?** Cross out 5 and write 4. **How many tenths do you have?** 12 Cross out the 2 and write 12.

- Have students subtract the tenths and ones and record the difference. **What is 5.2 − 3.6?** 1.6

- Provide students with a photocopy of the blank template. Have them find 9.4 − 6.7. 2.7

1 ENGAGE

Access Prior Knowledge Ask each student to name a favorite fruit. As a class, identify those fruits that are likely to be sold by the pound, and then discuss the accuracy that may be used to weigh the fruits. For example, is it reasonable for a store to round the weight to the nearest pound? What might be a more appropriate unit?

2 TEACH and TALK GO Online Animated Math Models

▶ **Unlock the Problem** MATHEMATICAL PRACTICES

In the activity, have students note the alignment of the decimal points in the vertical subtraction.

Discuss the quick pictures that students draw.

- **To complete this subtraction, why do you begin in the hundredths place?** Subtraction begins in the least (or rightmost) place value of the numbers.

- **Do you have to regroup to subtract hundredths? Explain how you know.** Yes; Possible explanation: There aren't enough hundredths to subtract 8 hundredths from 6 hundredths.

- **Describe the regrouping using place-value names.** Three tenths 6 hundredths are regrouped as 2 tenths 16 hundredths

Use **Math Talk** to focus on students' understanding of place value and regrouping. Extend the explanation by asking students to compare and contrast regrouping used during decimal subtraction to regrouping used during decimal addition.

COMMON CORE

CC.5.NBT.7 Add, subtract, multiply, and divide decimals to hundredths, using concrete models or drawings and strategies based on place value, properties of operations, and/or the relationship between addition and subtraction; relate the strategy to a written method and explain the reasoning used.

Name _____

Lesson **3.9**

Subtract Decimals

COMMON CORE STANDARD CC.5.NBT.7
Perform operations with multi-digit whole numbers and with decimals to hundredths.

Essential Question How can place value help you subtract decimals?

🔓 UNLOCK the Problem REAL WORLD

Hannah has 3.36 kilograms of apples and 2.28 kilograms of oranges. Hannah estimates she has about ① more kilogram of apples than oranges. How many more kilograms of apples than oranges does Hannah have? How can you use this estimate to decide if your answer is reasonable?

- What operation will you use to solve the problem?

  __subtraction__

- Circle Hannah's estimate to check that your answer is reasonable.

Subtract. 3.36 − 2.28

- Subtract the hundredths first. If there are not enough hundredths, regroup 1 tenth as 10 hundredths.

  __16__ hundredths − 8 hundredths = 8 hundredths

- Then subtract the tenths and ones. Regroup as needed.

  __2__ tenths − 2 tenths = 0 tenths

  __3__ ones − 2 ones = 1 one

$$\begin{array}{r} {\scriptstyle 2\,16} \\ 3.\cancel{3}\cancel{0} \\ -\ 2.28 \\ \hline 1.08 \end{array}$$

- Record the difference for each place value.

Draw a quick picture to check your work.

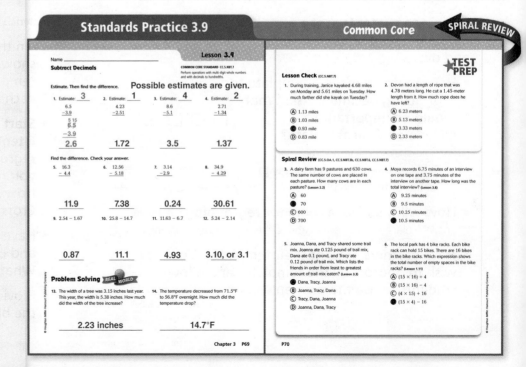

So, Hannah has __1.08__ more kilograms of apples than oranges.

Since __1.08__ is close to 1, the answer is reasonable.

Math Talk MATHEMATICAL PRACTICES
Explain how you know when to regroup in a decimal subtraction problem.

Possible explanation: I know that I need to regroup when I don't have enough hundredths or tenths to subtract from.

Chapter 3 **139**

Standards Practice 3.9 Common Core SPIRAL REVIEW

Name _____

Lesson **3.9**

Subtract Decimals

COMMON CORE STANDARD CC.5.NBT.7
Perform operations with multi-digit whole numbers and with decimals to hundredths.

Estimate. Then find the difference. **Possible estimates are given.**

1. Estimate: __3__

$$\begin{array}{r} 6.5 \\ -3.9 \\ \hline \begin{array}{r}{\scriptstyle 5\ 15}\\ \cancel{6}.\cancel{5}\\ -3.9 \\ \hline 2.6 \end{array} \end{array}$$

2. Estimate: __1__

$$\begin{array}{r} 4.23 \\ -2.51 \\ \hline 1.72 \end{array}$$

3. Estimate: __4__

$$\begin{array}{r} 8.6 \\ -5.1 \\ \hline 3.5 \end{array}$$

4. Estimate: __2__

$$\begin{array}{r} 2.71 \\ -1.34 \\ \hline 1.37 \end{array}$$

Find the difference. Check your answer.

5.
$$\begin{array}{r} 16.3 \\ -4.4 \\ \hline 11.9 \end{array}$$

6.
$$\begin{array}{r} 12.56 \\ -5.18 \\ \hline 7.38 \end{array}$$

7.
$$\begin{array}{r} 3.14 \\ -2.9 \\ \hline 0.24 \end{array}$$

8.
$$\begin{array}{r} 34.9 \\ -4.29 \\ \hline 30.61 \end{array}$$

9. 2.54 − 1.67

__0.87__

10. 25.8 − 14.7

__11.1__

11. 11.63 − 6.7

__4.93__

12. 5.24 − 2.14

__3.10, or 3.1__

Problem Solving REAL WORLD

13. The width of a tree was 3.15 inches last year. This year, the width is 5.38 inches. How much did the width of the tree increase?

__2.23 inches__

14. The temperature decreased from 71.5°F to 56.8°F overnight. How much did the temperature drop?

__14.7°F__

Chapter 3 **P69**

Lesson Check (CC.5.NBT.7) ★ TEST PREP

1. During training, Janice kayaked 4.68 miles on Monday and 5.61 miles on Tuesday. How much farther did she kayak on Tuesday?

Ⓐ 1.13 miles
Ⓑ 1.03 miles
● 0.93 mile
Ⓓ 0.83 mile

2. Devon had a length of rope that was 4.78 meters long. He cut a 1.45-meter length from it. How much rope does he have left?

Ⓐ 6.23 meters
Ⓑ 5.13 meters
● 3.33 meters
Ⓓ 2.33 meters

Spiral Review (CC.5.OA.1, CC.5.NBT.3b, CC.5.NBT.6, CC.5.NBT.7)

3. A dairy farm has 9 pastures and 630 cows. The same number of cows are placed in each pasture. How many cows are in each pasture? (Lesson 2.2)

Ⓐ 60
● 70
Ⓒ 600
Ⓓ 700

4. Moya records 6.75 minutes of an interview on one tape and 3.75 minutes of the interview on another tape. How long was the total interview? (Lesson 3.6)

Ⓐ 9.25 minutes
Ⓑ 9.5 minutes
Ⓒ 10.25 minutes
● 10.5 minutes

5. Joanna, Dana, and Tracy shared some trail mix. Joanna ate 0.125 pound of trail mix, Dana ate 0.1 pound, and Tracy ate 0.12 pound of trail mix. Which lists the friends in order from least to greatest amount of trail mix eaten? (Lesson 3.3)

● Dana, Tracy, Joanna
Ⓑ Joanna, Tracy, Dana
Ⓒ Tracy, Dana, Joanna
Ⓓ Joanna, Dana, Tracy

6. The local park has 4 bike racks. Each bike rack can hold 15 bikes. There are 16 bikes in the bike racks. Which expression shows the total number of empty spaces in the bike racks? (Lesson 1.11)

Ⓐ (15 × 16) + 4
Ⓑ (15 × 16) − 4
Ⓒ (4 × 15) + 16
● (15 × 4) − 16

P70

Try This! Use addition to check.

Since subtraction and addition are inverse operations, you can check subtraction by adding.

STEP 1	STEP 2
Find the difference.	**Check your answer.**
Subtract the hundredths first.	Add the difference to the number you subtracted. If the sum matches the number you subtracted from, your answer is correct.
Then, subtract the tenths, ones, and tens. Regroup as needed.	

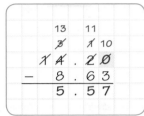

STEP 1:
```
     13  11
     ⫶  ⫶ 10
   X 4 . 2 Ø
 −   8 . 6 3
 ───────────
     5 . 5 7
```

STEP 2:
```
    1 1
    5.57   ← difference
 +  8.63   ← number subtracted
 ────────
   14.20   ← number subtracted from
```

• Is your answer correct? **Explain.**

Yes. Possible explanation: Because the difference added to the number I subtracted is

equal to the number I subtracted from, my answer is correct.

Share and Show

Estimate. Then find the difference. Possible estimates are given.

1. Estimate: __4__
```
   5.83
 −2.18
 ─────
   3.65
```

2. Estimate: __2__
```
   4.45
 −1.86
 ─────
   2.59
```

✓ 3. Estimate: __2__
```
   4.03
 −2.25
 ─────
   1.78
```

Find the difference. Check your answer.

4.
```
   0.70
 − 0.43
 ──────
   0.27
```

5.
```
   13.2
 − 8.04
 ──────
   5.16
```

✓ 6.
```
   15.8
 − 9.67
 ──────
   6.13
```

140

Reteach 3.9

Subtract Decimals

Subtract. 12.56 − 4.33

Step 1 Estimate the difference.
```
   12.56 − 4.33
     ↓      ↓
Estimate:  13  −  4  = 9
```

Step 2 Line up the place values for each number in a place-value chart. Then subtract.

	Ones	Tenths	Hundredths
	12	5	6
−	4	3	3
	8	2	3	←difference

Step 3 Use your estimate to determine if your answer is reasonable.

Think: 8.23 is close to the estimate, 9. The answer is reasonable.

So, 12.56 − 4.33 = __8.23__

Estimate. Then find the difference. Possible estimates are given.

1. Estimate: __1__
```
   1.97
 − 0.79
 ──────
   1.18
```

2. Estimate: __3__
```
   4.42
 − 1.26
 ──────
   3.16
```

3. Estimate: __2__
```
   10.25
 −  8.25
 ───────
   2.00 or 2
```

Find the difference. Check your answer.

4.
```
   5.75
 − 1.11
 ──────
   4.64
```

5.
```
   25.21
 − 19.05
 ───────
    6.16
```

6.
```
   42.14
 − 25.07
 ───────
   17.07
```

Enrich 3.9

In the Box Decimals

For 1–6, find the unknown numbers that make the subtraction sentence true.

1.
```
   1 4 7 . 0 [7]
 −   [4] 5 . 0 9
 ───────────────
   1 0 [1] . 9 8
```

2.
```
   [5] 8 3 . 4 1
 −   1 1 9 . 7 [7]
 ─────────────────
     4 [6] 3 . 6 4
```

3.
```
   9 4 2 . 9 9
 −   5 3 . 6 5
 ─────────────
   8 8 [9] . [3] 4
```

4.
```
   6 [9] 4 . 1 0
 −   5 2 9 . 1 [2]
 ─────────────────
   1 [6] 4 . 9 8
```

5.
```
   $ 1 [0] 2 4 . 1 [5]
 − $   4 4 5 . [9] 3
 ───────────────────
   $   5 7 [8] . 2 2
```

6.
```
   $ 8 [3] 4 . 9 2
 − $ [7] 5 6 . 0 [7]
 ───────────────────
   $   7 8 . 8 5
```

7. **Write Math** Explain how to subtract decimals.
Possible answer: line up the decimal points and place values. Then subtract. Regroup the numbers as needed. Place the decimal point.

8. **Stretch Your Thinking** Tell how you can check your answer for Exercise 1.
Possible answer: I can add 45.09 to the answer and check that the sum is 147.07.
101.98 + 45.09 = 147.07

Step 1 Ask students to explain why you use an equivalent decimal in order to subtract decimals. Possible answer: An equivalent decimal with the same value is used to keep place values aligned, and so that I can regroup to subtract.

Step 2 Have students describe each step of the addition process to ensure that they are regrouping properly.

3 PRACTICE

▶ **Share and Show • Guided Practice**

The first problem connects to the learning model. Have students use the MathBoard to explain their thinking.

Use Exercises 3 and 6 for **Quick Check.** Students should show their answers for the Quick Check on the Mathboard.

✓ **Quick Check** RtI

If → a student misses Exercises 3 and 6

Then → **Differentiate Instruction** with
• RtI Tier 1 Activity, p. 139B
• Reteach 3.9
★ Soar to Success Math 22.37

⚠ **COMMON ERRORS**

Error Students do not align place values correctly.

Example For 14.2 − 8.63, students do not record two decimal places in the answer.

Springboard to Learning Have students shade one column of a grid and write only decimal points in it. Encourage students to use a computational grid, grid paper, or lined paper turned sideways.

▶ On Your Own • Independent Practice

Remind students that making an estimate involves more than just approximating an answer—it also involves comparing the exact answer to the estimate and deciding if the answer is reasonable.

H.O.T. Problem Exercise 17 is different because it involves a known difference. Use the *solve a simpler problem* strategy to help students recognize how to solve for the unknown. Write the equation $7 - n = 5$ on the board and discuss how to find n.

- **Use mental math. What is the value of n?**
  The value of n is 2.

- **Suppose you did not know that n is 2. How could you find the value of n?** $7 - n = 5$ is related to $5 + n = 7$ and $7 - 5 = n$. Since $7 - 5 = 2$, $n = 2$.

Have students use the same understanding to solve for the unknown in Exercise 17.

Go Deeper

- **How can you subtract two decimal numbers with thousandths?** Possible answer: I align the place values, subtract, and regroup if necessary. Then I place the decimal point in the difference between the ones and tenths places.

Name _____

On Your Own ....

Estimate. Then find the difference. Possible estimates are given.

7. Estimate: __2__

$$\begin{array}{r} 4.08 \\ -1.74 \\ \hline 2.34 \end{array}$$

8. Estimate: __7__

$$\begin{array}{r} 13.54 \\ -\ 6.7 \\ \hline 6.84 \end{array}$$

9. Estimate: __12__

$$\begin{array}{r} 19.64 \\ -\ 8.12 \\ \hline 11.52 \end{array}$$

Find the difference. Check your answer.

10.
$$\begin{array}{r} 16.05 \\ -\ 1.5 \\ \hline 14.55 \end{array}$$

11.
$$\begin{array}{r} 7.3 \\ -5.4 \\ \hline 1.9 \end{array}$$

12.
$$\begin{array}{r} 21.4 \\ -16.97 \\ \hline 4.43 \end{array}$$

H.O.T. Find the difference.

13. three and seventy-two hundredths subtracted from five and eighty-one hundredths

2.09

14. one and six hundredths subtracted from eight and thirty-two hundredths

7.26

H.O.T. Algebra Write the unknown number for n.

15. $5.28 - 3.4 = n$

$n = $ ___1.88___

16. $n - 6.47 = 4.32$

$n = $ ___10.79___

17. $11.57 - n = 7.51$

$n = $ ___4.06___

Practice: Copy and Solve Find the difference.

18. $8.42 - 5.14$ 3.28

19. $16.46 - 13.87$ 2.59

20. $34.27 - 17.51$ 16.76

21. $15.83 - 11.45$ 4.38

22. $12.74 - 10.54$ 2.2

23. $48.21 - 13.65$ 34.56

© Houghton Mifflin Harcourt Publishing Company

Chapter 3 • Lesson 9   141

Cross-Curricular

SCIENCE

- Atoms are so small that it is not practical to measure the mass of one atom, so we measure an amount of atoms called a mole.

- A mole of iodine atoms has a mass of 126.9 grams. A mole of germanium atoms has a mass of 72.64 grams. What is the difference between the two masses? The difference between the mass of a mole of iodine and the mass of a mole of germanium is 54.26 grams.

SOCIAL STUDIES

- A market economy is based on the division of labor, and the prices of goods and services are determined in a free price system by supply and demand. In the early 1800s, prices were much lower than they are today. For instance, one dozen eggs may have been sold for $0.09, and a pair of boots may have been sold for $2.54.

- Do research to find the price of one dozen eggs and the price for a pair of boots now. What are the differences between the present prices of these items and the prices in the early 1800s. Answers should show an understanding of subtracting decimals to compare the prices.

 **Model • Reason • Make Sense**

🔓 UNLOCK the Problem REAL WORLD

24. In peanut butter, how many more grams of protein are there than grams of carbohydrates? Use the label at the right.

PEANUT BUTTER
Nutrition Facts
Serving Size 2 Tbsp (32.0 g)

Amount Per Serving	
Calories	190
Calories from Fat	190

	% Daily Value*
Total Fat 16g	**25%**
Saturated Fat 3g	**18%**
Polyunsaturated Fat 4.4g	
Monounsaturated Fat 7.8g	
Cholesterol 0mg	**0%**
Sodium 5mg	**0%**
Total Carbohydrates 6.2g	**2%**
Dietary Fiber 1.9g	**8%**
Sugars 2.5g	**8%**
Protein 8.1g	

*Based on a 2,000 calorie diet

a. What do you need to know? _how many_ _more grams of protein are in this_ _peanut butter than carbohydrates_

b. How will you use subtraction to find how many more grams of protein there are than grams of carbohydrates?

Possible answer: I will subtract the number of grams of carbohydrates from the number of grams of protein.

c. Show how you solved the problem.

$$\begin{array}{r} {\scriptstyle 7\ 11} \\ 8.\cancel{X} \\ -\ 6.2 \\ \hline 1.9 \end{array}$$

d. Complete each sentence.

The peanut butter has __8.1__ grams of protein.

The peanut butter has __6.2__ grams of carbohydrates.

There are __1.9__ more grams of protein than grams of carbohydrates in the peanut butter.

25. Kyle is building a block tower. Right now the tower stands 0.89 meter tall. How much higher does the tower need to be to reach a height of 1.74 meters?

0.85 meter

26. ⭐ Test Prep Allie is 158.7 centimeters tall. Her younger brother is 9.53 centimeters shorter than she is. How tall is Allie's younger brother?

- (A) 159.27 centimeters
- (B) 159.23 centimeters
- (C) 149.27 centimeters
- (D) 149.17 centimeters

© Houghton Mifflin Harcourt Publishing Company

142
FOR MORE PRACTICE:
Standards Practice Book, pp. P69–P70

FOR EXTRA PRACTICE:
Standards Practice Book, p. P77

► Unlock the Problem

Have students read the problem and discuss what they need to know.

In c., remind students

- of the importance of aligning place values before subtracting decimal numbers.
- to use addition to check the answer.

⭐ Test Prep Coach

In Exercise 26, if students selected:

A They didn't regroup the tenths and the tens correctly.

B They didn't regroup the tens correctly and didn't subtract the hundredths.

C They didn't regroup the tenths correctly.

4 SUMMARIZE

Essential Question

How can place value help you subtract decimals? Possible answer: Aligning the place values helps me subtract hundredths from hundredths, tenths from tenths, ones from ones, and so on.

Math Journal

Write a decimal subtraction problem that requires regrouping to solve. Then solve the problem.

Differentiated Instruction INDEPENDENT ACTIVITIES

Differentiated Centers Kit

Literature
Halfpipe

Students read about adding and subtracting decimals to rank snowboarders in a competition.

Games
Ride the Course

Students add or subtract decimals to move ahead on the course.

Digital Path

- 📺 Animated Math Models
- iT *i*Tools
- 〰️ HMH Mega Math
- ☆ Soar to Success Math
- GO eStudent Edition

Algebra • Patterns with Decimals

LESSON AT A GLANCE

Common Core Standard
Perform operations with multi-digit whole numbers and with decimals to hundredths.
CC.5.NBT.7 Add, subtract, multiply, and divide decimals to hundredths, using concrete models or drawings and strategies based on place value, properties of operations, and/or the relationship between addition and subtraction; relate the strategy to a written method and explain the reasoning used.

Lesson Objective
Identify, describe, and create numeric patterns with decimals.

Essential Question
How can you use addition or subtraction to describe a pattern or create a sequence with decimals?

Vocabulary sequence, term

Materials MathBoard

Digital Path

☑ Animated Math Models   🔵 eStudent Edition

Building Mathematical Practices

PROFESSIONAL DEVELOPMENT (COMMON CORE)

CC.K–12.MP.8 Look for and express regularity in repeated reasoning.

In this lesson students must look for repeated operations to identify patterns in number sequences and write rules to define those patterns. Students must also draw conclusions from patterns and pattern rules to identify unknown terms in number sequences.

Questions, such as the following, may help strengthen students' awareness of repeated reasoning in patterns and sequences:

- **What is the change from one term to the next?**

- **How can you write a rule so others could write more terms in this sequence?**

- **How can you use the rule to find an unknown term in the sequence?**

Daily Routines

Common Core

SPIRAL REVIEW

Problem of the Day

Test Prep Billy ran 100 yards in 12.8 seconds. Javon ran the same distance in 13.2 seconds. How much less was Billy's time than Javon's time?

Ⓐ 1.4 seconds

Ⓑ 1.2 seconds

⬤ 0.4 second

Ⓓ 0.2 second

Fluency Builder

Skip Counting by 7s, 9s, and 11s Have students take turns skip counting aloud by 7s, 9s, and 11s.

7, 14, 21, 28, 35, 42, 49, 56, 63, 70, 77, 84, 91, 98, 105, 112, 119, 126, 133, 140

9, 18, 27, 36, 45, 54, 63, 72, 81, 90, 99, 108, 117, 126, 135, 144, 153, 162, 171, 180

11, 22, 33, 44, 55, 66, 77, 88, 99, 110, 121, 132, 143, 154, 165, 176, 187, 198, 209, 220

Ask students to describe any patterns they notice in the counting sequences. Possible answers: In the 11s, the ones digit in each number increases by 1. In the 9s, the digits add up to 9.

This activity encourages mental addition rather than rote memorization of skip-counting sequences.

Differentiated Instruction Activities

ELL Language Support Visual / Linguistic Small Group

Strategy: Model Concepts

- Some students may use the words *extending* and *increasing* indistinguishably. Model both concepts to prevent misconceptions.

- Review that a sequence can be extended in different ways. **When you *extend* a sequence, you write more terms. A sequence can be *extended* by *adding* or also by *subtracting*.**

- Have students practice extending sequences that increase or decrease by a certain amount.

> *Add* 2 to *extend* this sequence:
> 2, 4, 6, ____, ____
>
> *Subtract* 3 to *extend* this sequence:
> 13, 10, 7, ____, ____

See **ELL** Activity Guide for leveled activities.

Enrich Logical / Mathematical Individual

- Challenge students to explore this sequence and find the rule and the next two terms.

    1, 1, 2, 3, 5, 8, 13, 21, 34, 55, 89, … After the first two terms, which are the same, each term is the sum of the two terms before it. 144, 233 are the next two terms.

- Tell students that this sequence is called a Fibonacci sequence. Have students who finish early use the rule to write the first six terms of a Fibonacci sequence starting with 1.3. 1.3, 1.3, 2.6, 3.9, 6.5, 10.4

 ## RtI Response to Intervention

Reteach Tier 1 Visual / Verbal Whole Class / Small Group

- Write 2.3, 3.5, 4.7, 5.9 on the board. **What do you notice about this sequence?** Possible answer: It is an increasing sequence; from one term to the next term the ones digit increases by 1 and the tenths digit increases by 2 tenths.

- **What can you do to find a rule for the sequence?** Possible answer: Subtract each term from the one that follows it and check whether the differences are the same.

- Have students find the differences. Discuss what the rule is. Add 1.2. **What are the next two terms? How do you find them?** 7.1, 8.3; I use the rule.

- Have students work in pairs to write sequences, exchange them, and find the rules for their partners' sequences.

Tier 2 Visual / Kinesthetic Small Group

Materials Dollar bills, Dimes (see *eTeacher Resources*)

- Show the money sequence $1.20, $2.30, $3.40, $4.50. **How do these money amounts increase?** Have students compare the amounts and help them see that each amount is $1.10 greater than the one before it.

- **The rule for this money sequence is *add $1.10*. What is the next term in the sequence?** $5.60

- **If you think of the bills as ones and the dimes as tenths, then the play money can show decimals. What are the decimals in the sequence?** 1.20, 2.30, 3.40, 4.50, 5.60

- Have students find the rule and next two terms for the sequence 1.3, 3.5, 5.7, 7.9. Add 2.2; 10.1, 12.3. Allow students to use play money to help.

① ENGAGE

Materials index cards

Access Prior Knowledge Ask students if they have ever rented canoes at a state park. Have students recall, if possible, the cost of renting a canoe.

- **How was the cost of renting a canoe determined?** Possible answer: The canoes are rented by the hour.

② TEACH and TALK 🔵 GO Online — Animated Math Models

▶ **Unlock the Problem** MATHEMATICAL PRACTICES

Have students discuss why the total price increases with each additional hour.

- **How does the cost of renting the canoe for 1 hour compare to the cost of renting the canoe for 2 hours?** It costs $1.75 more to rent a canoe for 2 hours than it does to rent a canoe for 1 hour.

- **How does the cost of renting the canoe for 2 hours compare to the cost of renting the canoe for 3 hours?** It costs $1.75 more to rent a canoe for 3 hours than it does to rent a canoe for 2 hours.

- **What statement can you make about the cost of renting a canoe as the rental time increases?** Possible answer: After the first hour, it costs $1.75 for each additional hour.

Ask students to identify the terms in the sequence. Make sure they understand that the sequence is made up of terms that follow a pattern, but the sequence is not the pattern. Help students see the relationship by identifying rules as patterns and the sequence as those numbers that follow the rule.

CC.5.NBT.7 Add, subtract, multiply, and divide decimals to hundredths, using concrete models or drawings and strategies based on place value, properties of operations, and/or the relationship between addition and subtraction; relate the strategy to a written method and explain the reasoning used.

Name _____

Patterns with Decimals

ALGEBRA
Lesson 3.10

Essential Question How can you use addition or subtraction to describe a pattern or create a sequence with decimals?

COMMON CORE STANDARD CC.5.NBT.7
Perform operations with multi-digit whole numbers and with decimals to hundredths.

⚡ UNLOCK the Problem REAL WORLD

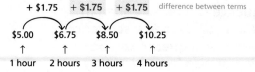

A state park rents canoes for guests to use at the lake. It costs $5.00 to rent a canoe for 1 hour, $6.75 for 2 hours, $8.50 for 3 hours, and $10.25 for 4 hours. If this pattern continues, how much should it cost Jason to rent a canoe for 7 hours?

A **sequence** is an ordered list of numbers. A **term** is each number in a sequence. You can find the pattern in a sequence by comparing one term with the next term.

STEP 1

Write the terms you know in a sequence. Then look for a pattern by finding the difference from one term in the sequence to the next.

```
     + $1.75   + $1.75   + $1.75    difference between terms

  $5.00    $6.75    $8.50    $10.25
    ↑        ↑        ↑         ↑
  1 hour  2 hours  3 hours  4 hours
```

STEP 2

Write a rule that describes the pattern in the sequence.

Rule: Possible rule: add $1.75

STEP 3

Extend the sequence to solve the problem.

$5.00, $6.75, $8.50, $10.25, __$12.00__, __$13.75__, __$15.50__

So, it should cost __$15.50__ to rent a canoe for 7 hours.

- What observation can you make about the pattern in the sequence that will help you write a rule?

  Possible answer: The terms are increasing by the same amount, so the rule

  includes addition.

© Houghton Mifflin Harcourt Publishing Company

Chapter 3   143

Standards Practice 3.10   Common Core   SPIRAL REVIEW

Name _____

Patterns with Decimals

ALGEBRA
Lesson 3.10

COMMON CORE STANDARD CC.5.NBT.7
Perform operations with multi-digit whole numbers and with decimals to hundredths.

Write a rule for the sequence. Then find the unknown term.

1. 2.6, 3.92, 5.24, __6.56__ 7.88

Think: 2.6 + ? = 3.92; 3.92 + ? = 5.24

2.6 + 1.32 = 3.92
3.92 + 1.32 = 5.24

Rule: __add 1.32__

2. 25.7, 24.1, __22.5__ 20.9, 19.3

Rule: __subtract 1.6__

3. 14.33, 13.22, 12.11, 11.00, __9.89__

Rule: __subtract 1.11__

4. 1.75 __4.25__ 6.75, 9.25, 11.75

Rule: __add 2.5__

Write the first four terms of the sequence.

5. **Rule:** start at 17.3, add 0.9

__17.3 18.2 19.1 20.0__

6. **Rule:** start at 28.6, subtract 3.1

__28.6 25.5 22.4 19.3__

Problem Solving REAL WORLD

7. The Ride-It Store rents bicycles. The cost is $8.50 for 1 hour, $13.65 for 2 hours, $18.80 for 3 hours, and $23.95 for 4 hours. If the pattern continues, how much will it cost Nate to rent a bike for 6 hours?

__$34.25__

8. Lynne walks dogs every day to earn money. The fees she charges per month are 1 dog, $40; 2 dogs, $37.25 each; 3 dogs, $34.50 each; 4 dogs, $31.75 each. A pet store wants her to walk 8 dogs. If the pattern continues, how much will Lynne charge to walk each of the 8 dogs?

__$20.75 each__

Chapter 3   P71

Lesson Check (CC.5.NBT.7)

1. A store has a sale on books. The price is $17.55 for one book, $16.70 each for 2 books, $15.85 each for 3 books, and $15 each for 4 books. If this pattern continues, how much will it cost to buy 7 books?

- (A) $14.15 each
- (B) $13.30 each
- (C) $13.15 each
- ● $12.45 each

2. A bowling alley offers special weekly bowling rates. The weekly rates are 5 games for $15, 6 games for $17.55, 7 games for $20.10, and 8 games for $22.65. If this pattern continues, how much will it cost to bowl 10 games in a week?

- (A) $25.20
- ● $27.75
- (C) $28.20
- (D) $37.95

Spiral Review (CC.5.NBT.5, CC.5.NBT.6, CC.5.NBT.7)

3. Find the product. (Lesson 1.7)

```
   284
 × 36
```

- (A) 2,556
- (B) 7,704
- (C) 9,224
- ● 10,224

4. At a sale, a shoe store sold 8 pairs of shoes for a total of $256. Each pair cost the same amount. What was the price of each pair of shoes? (Lesson 2.2)

- (A) $22
- ● $32
- (C) $248
- (D) $2,048

5. Marcie jogged 0.8 mile on Wednesday and 0.9 mile on Thursday. How far did she jog altogether? (Lesson 3.8)

- (A) 0.1 mile
- (B) 0.17 mile
- (C) 1.1 miles
- ● 1.7 miles

6. Bob has 5.5 cups of flour. He uses 3.75 cups of flour. How much flour does Bob have left? (Lesson 3.9)

- (A) 2.75 cups
- (B) 2.25 cups
- ● 1.75 cups
- (D) 1.25 cups

P72

🔑 **Example** Write a rule for the pattern in the sequence.
Then find the unknown terms in the sequence.

29.6, 28.3, 27, 25.7, **24.4**, **23.1**, **21.8**, 20.5, 19.2

STEP 1 Look at the first few terms in the sequence.

Think: Is the sequence increasing or decreasing
from one term to the next?

STEP 2 Write a rule that describes the pattern in the sequence.

What operation can be used to describe a sequence that increases?

addition

What operation can be used to describe a sequence that decreases?

subtraction

Rule: **Possible rule: subtract 1.3**

STEP 3 Use your rule to find the unknown terms.
Then complete the sequence above.

• **Explain** how you know whether your rule for a sequence
would involve addition or subtraction. **Possible explanation: If the sequence increases from one term to the next, the rule could involve addition. If the sequence decreases from one term to the next, the rule could involve subtraction.**

Try This!

Ⓐ Write a rule for the sequence. Then find the
unknown term.

65.9, 65.3, **64.7**, 64.1, 63.5, 62.9

Rule: **Possible rule: subtract 0.6**

Ⓑ Write the first four terms of the sequence.

Rule: start at 0.35, add 0.15

0.35, **0.50**, **0.65**, **0.80**

144

© Houghton Mifflin Harcourt Publishing Company

▶ **Example**

As students work on Step 2, ask:

• **Is the sequence increasing or decreasing?**
The sequence is decreasing.

• **Compare the differences from one term to the next. By what amount do the terms decrease?** 1.3

Remind students that a rule must describe the change from one term to the next for every pair of consecutive terms in a sequence. Have students describe how the terms in a sequence change and then write the sign to show the operation needed for the rule, such as "increasing" and an addition sign.

Try This!

A If students are having difficulty, first have them determine whether the pattern is increasing or decreasing. Then have them find the difference of the given values from one term to the next.

B If needed, help students by pointing out that, since the sequence starts at 0.35, the first term will be 0.35.

⚠️ **COMMON ERRORS**

Error When writing a sequence given a rule, students start at zero instead of the starting value.

Example In Try This! section B, the first term is 0.

Springboard to Learning Have students reread the rule before writing the sequence to make sure all of the details in the rule are accounted for, including the starting value.

 RtI

Reteach 3.10

Name _____

Lesson 3.10
Reteach

Algebra • Patterns with Decimals

Maria wants to download some songs from the Internet. The first song costs $1.50, and each additional song costs $1.20. How much will 2, 3, and 4 songs cost?

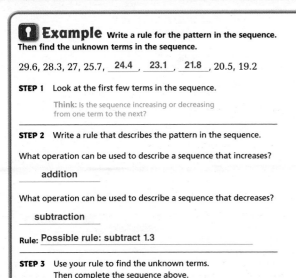

| Song 1 | Song 1 Song 2 | Song 1 Song 2 Song 3 | Song 1 Song 2 Song 3 Song 4 |
| 1 song $1.50 | 2 songs ? | 3 songs ? | 4 songs ? |

Step 1 Identify the first term in the sequence.
Think: The cost of 1 song is $1.50. The first term is $1.50.

Step 2 Identify whether the sequence is increasing or decreasing from one term to the next.
Think: Maria will pay $1.20 for each additional song.
The sequence is increasing.

Step 3 Write a rule that describes the sequence. Start with $1.50 and add $1.20.

Step 4 Use your rule to find the unknown terms in the sequence.

Number of Songs	1	2	3	4
Cost	$1.50	1.50 + 1.20 = $2.70	2.70 + 1.20 = $3.90	3.90 + 1.20 = $5.10

So, 2 songs cost $2.70, 3 songs cost $3.90, and 4 songs cost $5.10.

Write a rule for the sequence.

1. 0.4, 0.7, 1.0, 1.3, ...   Rule: **add 0.3**

2. 5.25, 5.00, 4.75, 4.50, ...   Rule: **subtract 0.25**

Write a rule for the sequence, then find the unknown term. Possible rules shown.

3. 26.1, 23.8, 21.5, **19.2**, 16.9   **subtract 2.3**

4. 4.62, 5.03, **5.44**, 5.85, 6.26   **add 0.41**

Reteach
© Houghton Mifflin Harcourt Publishing Company

R31

Grade 5

Enrich 3.10

Name _____

Lesson 3.10
Enrich

Pattern Match

Write the letter of the sequence that matches each clue.
Each sequence has 5 terms and is used exactly once.
Then write the unknown terms in the sequence.

	Clue		Sequence
d	1. Start at 1.2, end at 10.	**a.**	1.2, 1.15, **1.1** **1.05** **1**
f	2. Start at 8, add 0.3.	**b.**	6, 9.5, **13** **16.5** **20**
g	3. Start at 8.02, end at 8.22.	**c.**	**5** 4.8, **4.6** 4.4, **4.2**
h	4. Start at 4, subtract 0.02.	**d.**	1.2, 3.4, **5.6** **7.8** **10**
a	5. Start at 1.2, subtract 0.05.	**e.**	8.08, **8.06** **8.04** 8.02, **8**
c	6. Start at 5, end at 4.2.	**f.**	**8** 8.3, **8.6** 8.9, **9.2**
j	7. Subtract 2.4, end at 10.	**g.**	8.02, 8.07, **8.12** **8.17** **8.22**
b	8. Add 3.5, end at 20.	**h.**	**4** 3.98, **3.96** 3.94, **3.92**
e	9. Subtract 0.02, end at 8.	**i.**	**15** 14.6, **14.2** **13.8** 13.4
i	10. Start at 15, subtract 0.4.	**j.**	19.6, **17.2** **14.8** 12.4, **10**

11. ✏️Write Math ▶ Explain how you found the matching sequence in Exercise 6.
Possible answer: I looked for a decreasing sequence that had a 4 as the whole-number part in some of its terms. Sequence c fits, so I tried 5 as the first term. Using the rule "subtract 0.2," the sequence will end on 4.2.

Enrich
© Houghton Mifflin Harcourt Publishing Company

E31

Grade 5

Lesson 3.10 **144**

③ PRACTICE

▶ **Share and Show • Guided Practice**

The first problem connects to the learning model. Have students use the MathBoard to explain their thinking.

Use Exercises 2 and 6 for **Quick Check**.

✔ **Quick Check** 🔺 **RtI**

If ▶ a student misses Exercises 2 and 6

Then ▶ Differentiate Instruction with
- RtI Tier 1 Activity, p. 143B
- Reteach 3.10
- ☆ Soar to Success Math 27.24

▶ **On Your Own • Independent Practice**

Go Deeper

Give students the following sequence:
_____, 17.5, 13.3, 9.1, 4.9, 0.7

Ask students to find the unknown term. **21.7**

Then, have students explain how they got their answer. Possible explanation: I first noticed that the sequence is decreasing. Then I compared each term in the sequence to the next term to find a difference. I used the difference to write a rule and find the unknown term.

Name _____

Share and Show ....

Write a rule for the sequence. Possible rules are shown.

1. 0.5, 1.8, 3.1, 4.4, …

Think: Is the sequence increasing or decreasing?

Rule: add 1.3

⚫ 2. 23.2, 22.1, 21, 19.9, …

Rule: subtract 1.1

Write a rule for the sequence. Then find the unknown term.

3. 31.5, 25.2, 18.9, _12.6_ , 6.3

Rule: subtract 6.3

4. 0.25, 0.75, _1.25_ , 1.75, 2.25

Rule: add 0.50

5. 0.3, 1.5, _2.7_ , 3.9, 5.1

Rule: add 1.2

⚫ 6. 19.5, 18.8, 18.1, 17.4, _16.7_

Rule: subtract 0.7

Possible answer: Multiplication can result in an increase from one term to the next.

Math Talk **MATHEMATICAL PRACTICES** What operation, other than addition, suggests an increase from one term to the next?

On Your Own ....

Write a rule for the sequence. Then find the unknown term. Possible rules are shown.

7. 1.8, 4.1, _6.4_ , 8.7, 11

Rule: add 2.3

8. 6.85, 5.73, 4.61, _3.49_ , 2.37

Rule: subtract 1.12

9. 33.4, _31.1_ , 28.8, 26.5, 24.2

Rule: subtract 2.3

10. 15.9, 16.1, 16.3, _16.5_ , 16.7

Rule: add 0.2

Write the first four terms of the sequence.

11. Rule: start at 10.64, subtract 1.45

_10.64_ , _9.19_ , _7.74_ , _6.29_

12. Rule: start at 0.87, add 2.15

_0.87_ , _3.02_ , _5.17_ , _7.32_

13. Rule: start at 19.3, add 1.8

_19.3_ , _21.1_ , _22.9_ , _24.7_

14. Rule: start at 29.7, subtract 0.4

_29.7_ , _29.3_ , _28.9_ , _28.5_

© Houghton Mifflin Harcourt Publishing Company

Chapter 3 • Lesson 10   145

Problem Solving REAL WORLD ....

H.O.T. Pose a Problem

15. Bren has a deck of cards. As shown below, each card is labeled with a rule describing a pattern in a sequence. Select a card and decide on a starting number. Use the rule to write the first five terms in your sequence.

| Add 1.6 | Add 0.33 | Add 6.5 | Add 0.25 | Add 1.15 |

Sequence: Check students' sequences.
_____, _____, _____, _____, _____

Write a problem that relates to your sequence and requires the sequence be extended to solve.

Pose a Problem

Check students' problems.

Possible problem: Karen sells cookies.

One cookie costs $0.33. Two cookies

cost $0.58, and 3 cookies cost $0.83. If

this pattern continues, how much will 6

cookies cost?

Solve your problem.

Check students' work.

+0.25 +0.25

0.33,   0.58,   0.83,   ____,   ____,   ____

0.83 + 0.25 = 1.08

1.08 + 0.25 = 1.33

1.33 + 0.25 = 1.58

So, 6 cookies will cost $1.58.

• Explain how you solved your problem. Students' answers will vary depending on
their problems.

146 FOR MORE PRACTICE:
Standards Practice Book, pp. P71–P72

FOR EXTRA PRACTICE:
Standards Practice Book, p. P78

▶ **Problem Solving**
MATHEMATICAL PRACTICES

H.O.T. Problem Exercise 15 requires students to pose their own problem. Make sure students' problems are reasonable and make sense. Students may exchange papers with their classmates and solve each other's problems.

4 SUMMARIZE
MATHEMATICAL PRACTICES

Essential Question

How can you use addition or subtraction to describe a pattern or create a sequence with decimals? Possible answer: To describe a pattern, I need to analyze the differences between one term and the next. To create a sequence, I need to use the pattern rule provided, which includes the starting value.

Math Journal

Give an example of a rule describing the pattern for a sequence. Then write the terms of the sequence for your rule.

Differentiated Instruction **INDEPENDENT ACTIVITIES**

Grab-and-Go!

Differentiated Centers Kit

Activities
Get Around!

Students complete blue Activity Card 5 by adding decimals to find the perimeter of classroom objects.

Literature
A Hundredth of a Second

Students read about Olympic events in which competitors' times are just tenths or hundredths of a second apart.

Games
Ride the Course

Games

Students add or subtract decimals to move ahead on the course.

Digital Path

- Animated Math Models
- *i*T iTools
- HMH Mega Math
- Soar to Success Math
- *e*Student Edition

Problem Solving • Add and Subtract Money

LESSON AT A GLANCE

Common Core Standard
Perform operations with multi-digit whole numbers and with decimals to hundredths.
CC.5.NBT.7 Add, subtract, multiply, and divide decimals to hundredths, using concrete models or drawings and strategies based on place value, properties of operations, and/or the relationship between addition and subtraction; relate the strategy to a written method and explain the reasoning used.

Lesson Objective
Solve problems using the strategy *make a table*.

Essential Question
How can the strategy *make a table* help you organize and keep track of your bank account balance?

Materials MathBoard

Digital Path

- 🌐 Real World Video, Ch. 3
- *i*T *i*Tools: Measurement
- 🎞 Animated Math Models
- 👑 HMH Mega Math

COMMON CORE
PROFESSIONAL DEVELOPMENT

About the Math

Teaching for Depth Students learn many problem-solving strategies in their study of mathematics. Some strategies unlock a problem and enable it to be solved. Other strategies, such as making a table, are organizational tools. These organizational tools enable students to make sense of the data in a problem.

In this lesson, students will be presented with situations that involve a great deal of data; there is no single, correct way to organize the data. For example, some students may prefer to record deposits first. Regardless of their choices, tables enable students to more easily recognize the relationships that the data share.

Professional Development Video Podcasts

Daily Routines 📋 Math Board

Common Core

Problem of the Day
eTransparency **3.11**

Test Prep Jonah bought 3 new fish for his aquarium. The fish cost $4.85, $3.28, and $8.50. How much did Jonah spend in all?

- Ⓐ $25.50
- 🅑 $16.63
- Ⓒ $13.35
- Ⓓ $8.13

Fluency Builder

Counting Tape

Materials Counting Tape EVERY DAY **COUNTS**®

Ask a variety of questions to help students make connections between decimals and fractions. For example,

- Look at 0.40 and 0.04 on the Counting Tape. Which is greater? Why? 0.40 is greater because $\frac{40}{100}$ is greater than $\frac{4}{100}$.

- If 40% of the squares in a ten by ten grid are shaded, what percent of the squares are not shaded? 60%

- What coins could you use to make four-tenths of a dollar? Possible answer: 4 dimes

- How many more hundredths until we reach 0.50? How many tenths and hundredths is that? Answers will vary.

								0.4	
0.32	0.33	0.34	0.35	0.36	0.37	0.38	0.39	0.40	0.41
	$\frac{1}{3}$							$\frac{2}{5}$	

Differentiated Instruction Activities

ⓔ Language Support | Visual / Spatial Small Group

Strategy: Model Concepts

Materials Coins and Bills (see *eTeacher Resources*) (optional)

- Students understand concepts that are modeled. Have students use an organized table to help them find all of the possible coin combinations to make 27¢.

- Model for students how to set up their table.

Quarters	Dimes	Nickels	Pennies
0	2	1	2
0	2	0	7

- Help students complete the table and discuss the patterns they see.

- Ask: **How many ways are there?** 13 ways

See ⓔ **Activity Guide for leveled activities.**

Enrich | Visual / Social Small Group

- Have students consider businesses where money coming in and out should be tracked, such as a small business or a bank.

- Students should write a sample transaction record book for a possible month for the business they considered. For instance, if they chose a bakery, monthly expenses may include rent, employees' pay, and supplies needed; meanwhile, revenue would be coming in daily.

- Students may work together to model money going from one account to another.

- To extend the activity, have students tell a story using the transaction book.

ⓡⓣⓘ Response to Intervention

Reteach Tier 1 | Visual Whole Class / Small Group

Materials color pencils, checkbooks, transaction record book

- Students may not understand how the numbers on a check, in the transaction book, and on a statement relate to each other.

- Have groups write a check, using a different color pencil for each separate part. Then have students use the same colors to write the corresponding information in the transaction book.

- **Is there information in the transaction book that is not written on the check?** Yes. Possible answer: The account balance is not written on a check.

- Students may wish to look over sample bank statements and transaction books to compare the information shown on each one.

Tier 2 | Visual / Kinesthetic Small Group

Materials grid paper, Coins and Bills (see *eTeacher Resources*)

- Present this problem: **A gallon of milk costs $4.18. A loaf of bread costs $1.59. How much will you spend if you buy 2 gallons of milk and one a loaf of bread?**

- Have students work in pairs. Have one student answer the question using coins and bills and the other student answer using grid paper.

- **Compare the results of both methods as a group.** Both methods gave the same sum; $9.95.

- **Which method is easier? Which is faster?** Answers will vary.

				1	
	$	4	.	1	8
+	$	4	.	1	8
	$	8	.	¹3	6
+	$	1	.	5	9
	$	9	.	9	5

1 ENGAGE

 Real World Video, Ch. 3

Access Prior Knowledge Introduce the lesson by asking students:

Did you know that countries use different units of currency?

You may wish to share the following information with students:

The unit of currency used in the United States is the dollar. In other countries, different units of currency are used.

Units of currency may have different values, so a dollar may be worth more or less than a unit of another currency. The value of the unit of one currency compared to the unit of another currency can change from one day to the next. You can exchange dollars for units of another currency.

Country	Unit of Currency	Examples
Germany	euro	1 U.S. dollar = 0.75 euros
Japan	yen	1 U.S. dollar = 89 yen

Ask students how making a table could help them determine how much $1, $2, and $5 are worth in euros.

In this lesson, students will learn how to make a table to balance a checkbook.

2 TEACH and TALK

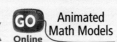 Animated Math Models

► Unlock the Problem

MATHEMATICAL PRACTICES

After students read the problem, give them an opportunity to discuss the relationship in the information. Make sure they understand that:

* the beginning balance is $442.37.
* a deposit and a withdrawal were made *after* the balance of $442.37 was established.
* writing a check decreases a balance.
* making a deposit increases a balance.

Discuss how the table presents the information in an organized, easy-to-understand way.

COMMON CORE

CC.5.NBT.7 Add, subtract, multiply, and divide decimals to hundredths, using concrete models or drawings and strategies based on place value, properties of operations, and/or the relationship between addition and subtraction; relate the strategy to a written method and explain the reasoning used.

Name _____

PROBLEM SOLVING Lesson 3.11

Problem Solving • Add and Subtract Money

Essential Question How can the strategy *make a table* help you organize and keep track of your bank account balance?

COMMON CORE STANDARD CC.5.NBT.7
Perform operations with multi-digit whole numbers and with decimals to hundredths.

🔓 UNLOCK the Problem REAL WORLD

At the end of May, Mrs. Freeman had an account balance of $442.37. Since then, she has written a check for $63.92 and made a deposit of $350.00. Mrs. Freeman says she has $729.45 in her account. Make a table to determine if Mrs. Freeman is correct.

Read the Problem	Solve the Problem
What do I need to find? I need to find if Mrs. Freeman's checkbook balance is correct.	**Mrs. Freeman's Checkbook**

Solve the Problem

Mrs. Freeman's Checkbook		
May balance		$442.37
Check	$63.92	−$63.92
		$378.45
Deposit		$350.00	+$350.00
Balance		728.45

What information do I need to use?

I need to use the starting account balance, the amount of the deposit, and the amount of the check.

How will I use the information?

I need to make a table and use the information to subtract the amount of the check and add the amount of the deposit to find the correct balance.

```
  $ 4 4 2 . 3 7
- $    6 3 . 9 2
  $ 3 7 8 . 4 5
+ $ 3 5 0 . 0 0
  $ 7 2 8 . 4 5
```

Mrs. Freeman's correct balance is $728.45 .

1. How can you tell if your answer is reasonable? Possible answer: I can use estimation to determine if my answer is reasonable.

© Houghton Mifflin Harcourt Publishing Company

Chapter 3 **147**

Standards Practice 3.11

Common Core SPIRAL REVIEW

Name _____

PROBLEM SOLVING Lesson 3.11

Problem Solving • Add and Subtract Money

COMMON CORE STANDARD CC.5.NBT.7
Perform operations with multi-digit whole numbers and with decimals to hundredths.

Solve. Use the table to solve 1–3.

1. Dorian and Jack decided to go bowling. They each need to rent shoes and 1 lane, and Jack is a member. If Jack pays for both of them with $20, what change should he receive?

   Calculate the cost: $7.50 + $3.95 + $2.95 = $14.40
   Calculate the change: $20 − $14.40 = $5.60

Bowl-a-Rama	Regular Cost	Member's Cost
Lane Rental (up to 4 people)	$9.75	$7.50
Shoe Rental	$3.95	$2.95

2. Natalie and her friends decided to rent 4 lanes at regular cost for a party. Ten people need to rent shoes, and 4 people are members. What is the total cost for the party?

   $74.50

3. Warren paid $23.85 and received no change. He is a member and rented 2 lanes. How many pairs of shoes did he rent?

   3 pairs of shoes

Use the following information to solve 4–6.

At the concession stand, medium sodas cost $1.25 and hot dogs cost $2.50.

4. Natalie's group brought in pizzas, but is buying the drinks at the concession stand. How many medium sodas can Natalie's group buy with $20? Make a table to show your answer.

   Check students' tables.
   16 sodas

5. Jack bought 2 medium sodas and 2 hot dogs. He paid with $20. What was his change?

   $12.50

6. How much would it cost to buy 3 medium sodas and 2 hot dogs?

   $8.75

Chapter 3 **P73**

TEST PREP

Lesson Check (CC.5.NBT.7)

1. Prakrit bought a pack of paper for $5.69 and printer toner for $9.76. He pair with a $20 bill. What was his change?

   (A) $5.55
   (B) $5.45
   ● $4.55
   (D) $4.45

2. Elysse paid for her lunch with a $10 bill and received $0.63 in change. The lunch special was $7.75. Sales tax was $0.47. What was the cost of her drink?

   ● $1.15
   (B) $1.97
   (C) $2.87
   (D) $2.97

Spiral Review (CC.5.NBT.3a, CC.5.NBT.4, CC.5.NF.*)

3. Tracie has saved $425 to spend during her 14-day vacation. About how much money can she spend each day? (Lesson 2.5)

   (A) $45
   (B) $42
   ● $30
   (D) $14

4. Which of the following decimals is $\frac{1}{10}$ of 0.08? (Lesson 3.1)

   (A) 8.0
   (B) 0.8
   (C) 0.18
   ● 0.008

5. Tyrone bought 2.25 pounds of Swiss cheese and 4.2 pounds of turkey at the deli. About how much was the weight of the two items? (Lesson 3.7)

   ● 6 pounds
   (B) 7 pounds
   (C) 8 pounds
   (D) 29 pounds

6. Shelly ate 4.2 ounces of trail mix. Marshall ate 4.25 ounces of trail mix. How much more trail mix did Marshall eat? (Lesson 3.9)

   (A) 0.45 ounce
   (B) 0.27 ounce
   (C) 0.23 ounce
   ● 0.05 ounce

P74

Try Another Problem

Nick is buying juice for himself and 5 friends. Each bottle of juice costs $1.25. How much does 6 bottles of juice cost? Make a table to find the cost of 6 bottles of juice.

Use the graphic below to solve the problem.

Read the Problem	Solve the Problem
What do I need to find? I need to find how much 6 bottles of juice will cost.	Possible table shown.

Solve the Problem:

Bottles of Juice	Total
1	$1.25
2	$2.50
3	$3.75
4	$5.00
5	$6.25
6	$7.50

What information do I need to use?

I need to use the price of each bottle and the number of bottles being bought.

How will I use the information?

I will make a table and then add the amount per bottle until I find the cost of 6 bottles of juice.

So, the total cost of 6 bottles of juice is _____ $7.50 _____.

2. What if Ginny says that 12 bottles of juice cost $25.00? Is Ginny's statement reasonable? Explain. No, Ginny's statment is not reasonable. Possible explanation: I know that 6 bottles of juice cost $7.50, so twice as many bottles of juice would cost $15.00.

3. If Nick had $10, how many bottles of juice could he buy? _____ 8 bottles

Possible explanation: I could draw a diagram using coins and bills for the cost of each bottle of juice.

 Math Talk MATHEMATICAL PRACTICES Explain how you could use another strategy to solve this problem.

© Houghton Mifflin Harcourt Publishing Company

148

Have students discuss and answer the questions in the graphic organizer. Before they make the table, have them recall how to regroup when adding decimal numbers.

- **Explain how to regroup hundredths when adding.** If the value of the digit in the hundredths place in the sum is 10 or more, regroup 10 hundredths as 1 tenth.

- **Explain how to regroup tenths when adding.** If the value of the digit in the tenths place in the sum is 10 or more, regroup 10 tenths as 1 one.

- **When you add money, what place value do pennies represent?** Pennies represent hundredths of a dollar.

- **What place value do dimes represent?** Dimes represent tenths of a dollar.

Use **Math Talk** to focus on students' understanding of other problem-solving strategies they can use.

 Portfolio You may suggest that students place completed Try Another Problem graphic organizers in their portfolios.

Reteach 3.11

Name _____ Lesson 3.11 Reteach

Problem Solving • Add and Subtract Money

At the end of April, Mrs. Lei had a balance of $476.05. Since then she has written checks for $263.18 and $37.56, and made a deposit of $368.00. Her checkbook balance currently shows $498.00. Find Mrs. Lei's correct balance.

Read the Problem	Solve the Problem
What do I need to find? I need to find Mrs. Lei's correct checkbook balance	**Balancing Mrs. Lei's Checkbook**

		Balancing Mrs. Lei's Checkbook
April balance		$476.05
Deposit	$368.00	+$368.00
		$844.05
Check	$263.18	−$263.18
		$580.87
Check	$37.56	−$37.56
		$543.31

What information do I need to use?
I need to use the April balance, and the check and deposit amounts

How will I use the information?
I need to make a table and use the information to subtract the checks and add the deposit to find the correct balance

Mrs. Lei's correct balance is $543.31

1. At the end of June, Mr. Kent had a balance of $375.98. Since then he has written a check for $38.56 and made a deposit of $408.00. His checkbook shows a balance of $645.42. Find Mr. Kent's correct balance.

$745.42

2. Jordan buys a notebook for himself and each of 4 friends. Each notebook costs $1.85. Make a table to find the cost of 5 notebooks.

$9.25

Reteach R32 Grade 5
© Houghton Mifflin Harcourt Publishing Company

Enrich 3.11

Name _____ Lesson 3.11 Enrich

Balancing Act

Make and complete a table to solve. Check students' work.

1. Felicia wants to buy a new soccer ball. It is on sale for $12.60. She has a $10 bill, two $5 bills, three $1 bills, 6 quarters, and 3 nickels. Make a table to find four ways she could pay for the soccer ball.

$10 bills	$5 bills	$1 bills	Quarters	Nickels	Total
1	0	2	2	2	$12.60
1	0	1	6	2	$12.60
0	2	2	2	2	$12.60
0	2	1	6	2	$12.60

2. Since his January statement, Mr. Park has written two checks for $6,098.11 and $3,876.99 and made a deposit. His January statement shows a balance of $12,897.55, and his checkbook balance shows he currently has $6,984.85. How much did Mr. Park deposit? $4,062.40

Balancing Mr. Park's Checkbook
January balance

3. Mrs. Chen wrote two checks and made a deposit of $1,987.09 since her October statement. The October statement shows a balance of $3,611.08, and her checkbook balance shows she currently has $2,778.69. What is the total amount of the checks that Mrs. Chen wrote? $2,819.48

Balancing Mrs. Chen's Checkbook
October balance

4. **Stretch Your Thinking** Explain how you could use another strategy to solve Exercise 3.
Possible answer: I could work backward to solve the problem.

Enrich E32 Grade 5
© Houghton Mifflin Harcourt Publishing Company

⚠ **COMMON ERRORS**

Error Students omit some of the given data from a table.

Example Students record the cost of 5 bottles of juice instead of 6.

Springboard to Learning Before adding the numbers in the table, have students count to make sure the number of bottles of juice in the table matches the number of bottles given in the problem.

3 PRACTICE Math Board

▶ **Share and Show • Guided Practice**

The first problem connects to the learning model. Have students use the MathBoard to explain their thinking. Check students' tables to ensure that each combination is unique and has a value of $2.30.

After students solve the problem, invite volunteers to name different strategies that they selected, and explain how they used those strategies.

Use Exercises 2 and 3 for Quick Check.

 Quick Check ▲ RtI

If ▶ a student misses Exercises 2 and 3

Then ▶ **Differentiate Instruction with**
- RtI Tier 1 Activity, p. 147B
- Reteach 3.11
- ⭐ Soar to Success Math 61.04

Share and Show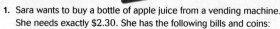

1. Sara wants to buy a bottle of apple juice from a vending machine. She needs exactly $2.30. She has the following bills and coins: **Possible tables shown.**

Make and complete a table to find all the ways Sara could pay for the juice.

First, draw a table with a column for each type of bill or coin.

Next, fill in your table with each row showing a different way Sara can make exactly $2.30.

$1 bills	Quarters	Dimes	Nickels	Value
2	1	0	1	$2.30
2	0	2	2	$2.30
1	5	0	1	$2.30
1	4	2	2	$2.30

✓ 2. What if Sara decides to buy a bottle of water that costs $1.85? What are all the different ways she can make exactly $1.85 with the bills and coins she has? Which coin must Sara use?

$1 bills	Quarters	Dimes	Nickels	Value
1	3	1	0	$1.85
1	3	0	2	$1.85

quarter

✓ 3. At the end of August, Mr. Diaz had a balance of $441.62. Since then, he has written two checks for $157.34 and $19.74 and made a deposit of $575.00. Mr. Diaz says his balance is $739.54. Find Mr. Diaz's correct balance.

Balancing Mr. Diaz's Checkbook

August balance			$441.62
Deposit		$575.00	$575.00
			$1,016.62
Check	$157.34		$157.34
			$859.28
Check	$19.74		$19.74
			$839.54

Mr. Diaz's correct balance is $839.54.

© Houghton Mifflin Harcourt Publishing Company

Math Talk in Action

Teacher: How did you find Mr. Diaz's correct balance in Exercise 3?

Pete: I made a table and listed the starting balance, the amount of the deposit, and the amounts of the checks. By looking at the amounts being added and subtracted, I think the amount Mr. Diaz gave for his account balance is too low. So, he probably made a mistake in adding the deposit.

Elena: Yes; the correct balance was $100 more than his. So, I think he just made a mistake.

Teacher: Right. Mr. Diaz made the mistake when doing the math, or computation. How did using the table keep you from making the same mistake?

Pete: I was able to organize the numbers and keep track of each transaction.

Elena: I marked each number as I added or subtracted it from the balance. The table made it easy for me to see what I had done.

Teacher: How can you check that your answer is reasonable?

Rob: I can estimate each amount and recalculate. If my estimate is close to the final balance, then my answer is reasonable.

Bethany: I thought of a way of making sure my answer is correct. I can start with the final balance and work backward using inverse operations. If my answer is correct, I should wind up with the original balance.

Teacher: The table will help with both of those methods, too. Good work, everyone.

On Your Own . . . .

Use the following information to solve 4–7.

At Open Skate Night, admission is $3.75 with a membership card and $5.00 without a membership card. Skate rentals are $3.00.

Choose a STRATEGY

Act It Out
Draw a Diagram
Make a Table
Solve a Simpler Problem
Work Backward
Guess, Check, and Revise

4. Aidan paid the admission for himself and two friends at Open Skate Night. Aidan had a membership card, but his friends did not. Aidan paid with a $20 bill. How much change should Aidan receive?

$6.25

5. The Moores and Cotters were at Open Skate Night. The Moores paid $6 more for skate rentals than the Cotters did. Together, the two families paid $30 for skate rentals. How many pairs of skates did the Moores rent?

6 pairs of skates

6. ⚠H.O.T. Jennie and 5 of her friends are going to Open Skate Night. Jennie does not have a membership card. Only some of her friends have membership cards. What is the total amount that Jennie and her friends might pay for admission?

Answers will vary. Possible answer: They

will pay $27.50 if only 2 of her friends have

membership cards.

 SHOW YOUR WORK

7. ⭐ Test Prep Sean and Hope each have a membership card for Open Skate Night. Sean has his own skates, but Hope will have to rent skates. Sean gives the clerk $15 for their admission and skate rental. How much change should he receive?

Ⓐ $3.50   Ⓒ $5.00
🅑 $4.50   Ⓓ $6.50

FOR EXTRA PRACTICE: Standards Practice Book, p. P78

© Houghton Mifflin Harcourt Publishing Company

▶ **On Your Own • Independent Practice**

H.O.T. Problem Exercise 6 is a multistep problem that has more than one possible answer. The answers students find depend on how they interpret the word *some*. For example, we are told that some of Jennie's friends have membership cards, but we are also told that not all of the five friends have cards, so the number of friends with cards is 2, 3, or 4.

⭐ Test Prep Coach

In Exercise 7, if students selected:

A They added the price with membership cards incorrectly.
C They used non-membership card prices without renting skates.
D They subtracted the price with membership cards and a skate rental incorrectly.

 4 SUMMARIZE (MATHEMATICAL PRACTICES)

Essential Question

How can the strategy *make a table* help you organize and keep track of your bank account balance? Possible answer: I can use a table to record balances, add deposits, and subtract checks.

Math Journal

Write a money problem that shows money being added to and subtracted from a bank account. Then solve the problem.

  Differentiated Instruction INDEPENDENT ACTIVITIES

Grab-and-Go!™

Differentiated Centers Kit

Activities
Add-A-Round

Students complete orange Activity Card 5 by finding decimal addends that equal a given sum.

Literature
Halfpipe

Students read about adding and subtracting decimals to rank snowboarders in a competition.

Games
Ride the Course

Students add or subtract decimals to move ahead on the course.

Digital Path

🖥 Animated Math Models
iT iTools
MM HMH Mega Math
⭐ Soar to Success Math
GO Math eStudent Edition

Choose a Method

LESSON AT A GLANCE

Common Core Standard
Perform operations with multi-digit whole numbers and with decimals to hundredths.
CC.5.NBT.7 Add, subtract, multiply, and divide decimals to hundredths, using concrete models or drawings and strategies based on place value, properties of operations, and/or the relationship between addition and subtraction; relate the strategy to a written method and explain the reasoning used.

Lesson Objective
Choose a method to find a decimal sum or difference.

Essential Question
Which method could you choose to find decimal sums and differences?

Materials MathBoard

Digital Path

☑ **Animated Math Models**   🔤 **eStudent Edition**

PROFESSIONAL DEVELOPMENT
COMMON CORE

About the Math

Teaching for Depth To perform the computations in this lesson, students choose to use mental math, paper and pencil, or a calculator. Using paper and pencil involves the ability to recognize the place value of numbers and understand how to decompose them, as well as represent them in different ways. It also involves understanding relationships among operations.

Although students generally choose a calculator for computation with large numbers, presenting them with a variety of computation situations will help them build a set of strategies that can be used for both solving problems and checking computations for reasonableness.

PODCASTING

Professional Development Video Podcasts

Daily Routines
Math Board

Common Core

SPIRAL REVIEW

Problem of the Day

eTransparency
3.12

Test Prep Peter measured 1.7 centimeters of rain in the first week of August. He measured 2.2 centimeters of rain in the second week of August. About how much rain fell in the first two weeks of August?

Ⓐ about 2 centimeters

Ⓑ about 3 centimeters

Ⓒ about 4 centimeters

Ⓓ about 5 centimeters

Vocabulary Builder

Materials Vocabulary Cards (see *eTeacher Resources*)

Use vocabulary cards to help students remember definitions for review words.

Ask students to respond to a question or statement such as:

In what sort of problem might you use…?

How would you know to use…?

Associative Property of Addition	Commutative Property of Addition

Differentiated Instruction Activities

ELL Language Support

 Visual
Small Group

Strategy: Identify Relationships

- Students can make connections between problems to describe and apply methods for solving problems.

- Describe each step to solve three problems using three methods: the properties and mental math, paper and pencil, and a calculator.

- Show students a problem. Have them explain which method they would choose and why. Make sure they identify the relationship between the problem and one of the examples.

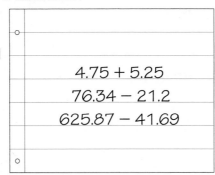

$4.75 + 5.25$

$76.34 - 21.2$

$625.87 - 41.69$

See **ELL** Activity Guide for leveled activities.

Enrich

 Logical
Small Group

Have students use each of the digits 1–8 once in the following addition problem. Students should use the various methods to help them.

Possible answer: 75.38 + 26.14

Have students make up similar problems to share with classmates.

 RtI Response to Intervention

Reteach Tier 1

 Auditory
Whole Class / Small Group

Materials calculators

- Display **5.75 + 3.25**. Ask: **Why is mental math a good method to use to find the sum?** The decimals add to make a whole number. **Have students find the sum by using mental math.** 9

- Display **13.06 − 7.89**. Ask: **Why might you use a calculator to find the difference?** The numbers are not easy to compute mentally because you need to regroup to subtract. **Have students find the difference. Remind students to enter the decimal point in the calculator.** 5.17

- Paper and pencil would also be a good choice for finding 13.06 − 7.89. Have students write the problem vertically, aligning the place-value positions. Remind students to place the decimal point in the difference.

Tier 2

 Visual
Small Group

Materials calculator

- Write these problems on the board: 3.86 − 1.19; 4.3 + 5.7; 1.25 + 2.5.

- Discuss each possible method for adding and subtracting decimals with students: pencil and paper, mental math, calculator. **When is each method helpful?** Answers will vary.

- **Which problem includes numbers we use often with money?** 1.25 + 2.5. **Solve the addition mentally.** 1.25 + 2.5 = 3.75

- **Which expression involves regrouping?** 3.86 − 1.19

- **Which method is best for solving 4.3 + 5.7?** Since the decimals add to 1.0, mental math is appropriate.

1 ENGAGE

Access Prior Knowledge Point out that a problem in today's lesson involves a track-and-field event known as the long jump. Invite volunteers to suggest what a long jump might entail. A long jump involves one jump. A long jumper runs down a path to a take-off point, jumps as far as possible, and lands in a sand pit.

2 TEACH and TALK GO Online Animated Math Models

▶ Unlock the Problem MATHEMATICAL PRACTICES

How far is a good long jump? Read the problem to learn the distances one person jumped.

When students name the operation they will use, ask them to give a reason to support their answer.

▶ One Way

- **What does the Commutative Property of Addition allow you to do?** change the order of two addends
- **What does the Associative Property of Addition allow you to do?** change the way addends are grouped

▶ Another Way

Remind students of the importance of aligning place values whenever they add or subtract decimal numbers.

Use Math Talk to focus on students' understanding of when to use properties to solve problems.

CC.5.NBT.7 Add, subtract, multiply, and divide decimals to hundredths, using concrete models or drawings and strategies based on place value, properties of operations, and/or the relationship between addition and subtraction; relate the strategy to a written method and explain the reasoning used.

Name _____

Choose a Method

Lesson 3.12

Essential Question Which method could you choose to find decimal sums and differences?

COMMON CORE STANDARD CC.5.NBT.7
Perform operations with multi-digit whole numbers and with decimals to hundredths.

UNLOCK the Problem REAL WORLD

At a track meet, Steven entered the long jump. His jumps were 2.25 meters, 1.81 meters, and 3.75 meters. What was the total distance Steven jumped?

To find decimal sums, you can use properties and mental math or you can use paper and pencil.

- Underline the sentence that tells you what you are trying to find.
- Circle the numbers you need to use.
- What operation will you use?
  addition

🔒 One Way Use properties and mental math.

Add. 2.25 + 1.81 + 3.75

$$2.25 + 1.81 + 3.75$$
$$= 2.25 + 3.75 + 1.81 \quad \text{Commutative Property}$$
$$= (\underline{2.25} + \underline{3.75}) + 1.81 \quad \text{Associative Property}$$
$$= \underline{6.00} + 1.81$$
$$= \underline{7.81}$$

🔒 Another Way Use place-value.

Add. 2.25 + 1.81 + 3.75

```
  1 1
  2.25
  1.81
+ 3.75
  7.81
```

So, the total distance Steven jumped was ____7.81____ meters.

Math Talk MATHEMATICAL PRACTICES
Explain why you might choose to use the properties to solve this problem.

Possible explanation: Since 0.75 + 0.25 make 1 whole, it is easier and quicker to use the properties to find the sum.

Chapter 3 151

Standards Practice 3.12 Common Core SPIRAL REVIEW

Name _____

Choose a Method

COMMON CORE STANDARD CC.5.NBT.7
Perform operations with multi-digit whole numbers and with decimals to hundredths.

Lesson 3.12

Find the sum or difference.

1. 7.24 +3.18	2. 5.2 6.47 +12.16	3. 6.37 −4.98	4. 0.64 9.68 +1.47
7.24 +3.18			
10.42	23.83	1.39	11.79

5. 14.87 +3.65	6. 60.12 −14.05	7. 2.72 +9.48	8. 16.85 +83.4
18.52	46.07	12.20	100.25

9. $13.60 − $8.74 **$4.86**

10. $25.00 − $16.32 **$8.68**

11. 13.65 + 6.90 + 4.35 **24.90**

Problem Solving REAL WORLD

12. Jill bought 6.5 meters of blue lace and 4.12 meters of green lace. What was the total length of lace she bought?

10.62 meters

13. Zack bought a coat for $69.78. He paid with a $100 bill and received $26.73 in change. How much was the sales tax?

$3.49

Chapter 3 P75

★TEST PREP

Lesson Check (CC.5.NBT.7)

1. Jin buys 4 balls of yarn for a total of $23.78. She pays with two $20 bills. What is her change?
   - (A) $1.78
   - (B) $3.78
   - ● $16.22
   - (D) $18.22

2. Allan is measuring his dining room table to make a tablecloth. The table is 0.45 meter longer than it is wide. If it is 1.06 meters wide, how long is it?
   - (A) 1.51 meters
   - (B) 1.41 meters
   - (C) 1.01 meters
   - (D) 1.10 meters

Spiral Review (CC.5.NBT.6, CC.5.NBT.7)

3. Which of the following can be used to find 56 ÷ 4? (Lesson 1.9)
   - (A) (4 × 7) + (4 × 8)
   - (B) (4 × 50) + (4 × 6)
   - (C) (2 × 28) + (2 × 2)
   - ● (4 × 10) + (4 × 4)

4. Jane, Andre, and Maria pick apples. Jane picks three times as many pounds as Maria. Jane picks two times as many pounds as Andre. The total weight of the apples is 840 pounds. How many pounds of apples does Andre pick? (Lesson 2.9)
   - (A) 84 pounds
   - ● 252 pounds
   - (C) 504 pounds
   - (D) 840 pounds

5. What is the sum of 6.43 and 0.89? (Lesson 3.8)
   - (A) 5.54
   - (B) 6.22
   - (C) 6.32
   - ● 7.32

6. Hannah bought a total of 5.12 pounds of fruit at the market. She bought 2.5 pounds of pears, and she also bought some bananas. How many pounds of bananas did she buy? (Lesson 3.9)
   - (A) 2.37 pounds
   - ● 2.62 pounds
   - (C) 3.37 pounds
   - (D) 3.5 pounds

P76

© Houghton Mifflin Harcourt Publishing Company

Try This!

In 1924, William DeHart Hubbard won a gold medal with a long jump of 7.44 meters. In 2000, Roman Schurenko won the bronze medal with a jump of 8.31 meters. How much longer was Schurenko's jump than Hubbard's?

A Use place-value.

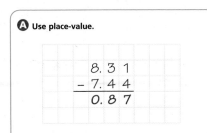

$$\begin{array}{r} 8.31 \\ -7.44 \\ \hline 0.87 \end{array}$$

B Use a calculator.

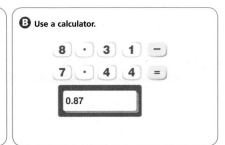

So, Schurenko's jump was ___0.87___ meter longer than Hubbard's.

- **Explain** why you cannot use the Commutative Property or the Associative Property to find the difference between two decimals.

  Possible explanation: When you subtract, if you change the order of the numbers or you

  group the numbers in a different way, you do not end up with the same answer.

Share and Show

Find the sum or difference.

1. 4.19 + 0.58
   4.77

2. 9.99 − 4.1
   5.89

✓ 3. 5.7 + 2.25 + 1.3
   9.25

4. 28.6 − 9.84
   18.76

5. $15.79 + $32.81
   $48.60

✓ 6. 38.44 − 25.86
   12.58

152

© Houghton Mifflin Harcourt Publishing Company

Try This!

In this example, students subtract decimals in two different ways.

A Why is it important to align place values to subtract decimals using paper and pencil?
It ensures that we subtract the correct digits.

B Remind students that they should use an estimate to check the reasonableness of their answer when using a calculator. If their answer is not reasonable, they need to check that they entered the values into the calculator correctly.

▶ **Share and Show • Guided Practice**

The first problem connects to the learning model. Have students use the MathBoard to explain their thinking.

Use Exercises 3 and 6 for **Quick Check**. Students should show their answers for the Quick Check on the MathBoard.

✓ Quick Check  RtI

If ➤ a student misses Exercises 3 and 6

Then ➤ **Differentiate Instruction** with
- RtI Tier 1 Activity, p. 151B
- Reteach 3.12
- Soar to Success Math 22.40

Reteach 3.12 RtI

Name _____

Lesson 3.12
Reteach

Choose a Method

There is more than one way to find the sums and differences of whole numbers and decimals. You can use properties, mental math, place value, a calculator, or paper and pencil.

Choose a method. Find the sum or difference.

- Use mental math for problems with fewer digits or rounded numbers.

  $$\begin{array}{r} 2.86 \\ -1.2 \\ \hline 1.66 \end{array}$$

- Use place value for larger numbers.

  $$\begin{array}{r} \$15.79 \\ +\$32.81 \\ \hline \$48.60 \end{array}$$

- Use a calculator for difficult numbers or very large numbers.

  [3][8][.][4][4][−][2][5][.][8][6][=] 12.58

Find the sum or difference.

1. 73.9
   + 4.37
   78.27

2. 127.35
   + 928.52
   1,055.87

3. 10
   + 2.25
   12.25

4. 0.36
   + 1.55
   1.91

5. 71.4
   + 11.5
   82.9

6. 90.4
   + 88.76
   179.16

7. 3.3
   + 5.6
   8.9

8. 14.21
   1.79
   + 15.88
   31.88

9. 68.20 − 42.10
   26.10

10. 2.25 − 1.15
    1.10

11. 875.33 − 467.79
    407.54

12. 97.26 − 54.90
    42.36

Reteach
© Houghton Mifflin Harcourt Publishing Company

R33

Grade 5

Enrich 3.12

Name _____

Lesson 3.12
Enrich

Decimal Dance

Use mental math, place value, or a calculator to solve 1–12. Write each sum or difference in the top box of the next column until you finish the last exercise in each row.

1. 8.29
   + 12.15
   20.44

2. 20.44
   − 7.12
   13.32

3. 13.32
   + 16.78
   30.10

30.10
+ 2.9
33

4. 46.23
   − 19.82
   26.41

5. 26.41
   + 5.48
   31.89

6. 31.89
   − 8.32
   23.57

23.57
4.2
+ 6.37
34.14

7. 15.89
   − 5.91
   9.98

8. 9.98
   − 6.58
   3.4

9. 3.4
   + 18.60
   22

22
− 12.46
9.54

10. 92.46
    − 29.32
    63.14

11. 63.14
    19
    + 5.87
    88.01

12. 88.01
    − 8.01
    80

80
− 70.99
9.01

13. **Write Math** What if the first number in Exercise 1 were 8.39? How would the sums and differences in the first row change?
    Possible answer: each number that I wrote in that row would be 0.1 greater than the number shown.

Enrich
© Houghton Mifflin Harcourt Publishing Company

E33

Grade 5

⚠ COMMON ERRORS

Error The number of decimal places in a sum or difference is not correct.

Example Students write a difference of 8.7 when subtracting 7.44 from 8.31.

Springboard to Learning Make sure students understand how estimates and inverse operations can be used to check their answers. An estimate of the difference (1) would have indicated that their answer was not correct.

③ PRACTICE Math Board

▶ On Your Own • Independent Practice

If students complete Exercises 3 and 6 correctly, they may continue with Independent Practice. Remind students of the importance of checking their work.

- **How can you use an estimate to check the reasonableness of the answer you find for Exercise 7?** Possible answer: Round $18.39 to $18, round $7.56 to $8, and then compare $26, the estimate of the sum, to the exact answer.

- **How can you use an inverse operation to check your answer in Exercise 8?** Add 4.39 to the exact answer; if the sum is 8.22, the answer checks.

H.O.T. Problems Exercises 27–29 involve solving an equation for an unknown. Some students may find it helpful to first *solve a simpler problem* by writing and solving a related problem using the inverse operation. For example, point out that the value of n in the equation $n + 1 = 10$ can be found by writing and solving a related problem $10 - 1 = 9$. So, $n = 9$.

To find the value of n in Exercise 29, students must first find the sum of 9.2 and 8.4 before using inverse operations to solve the equation.

Name _____

On Your Own

Find the sum or difference.

7.
$$\begin{array}{r} \$18.39 \\ +\$\ 7.56 \\ \hline \$25.95 \end{array}$$

8. $8.22 - 4.39$
3.83

9. $93.6 - 79.84$
13.76

10.
$$\begin{array}{r} 1.82 \\ 2.28 \\ +2.18 \\ \hline 6.28 \end{array}$$

11.
$$\begin{array}{r} 2.35 \\ -0.16 \\ \hline 2.19 \end{array}$$

12.
$$\begin{array}{r} 5.16 \\ +4.54 \\ \hline 9.70 \end{array}$$

13.
$$\begin{array}{r} 15.3 \\ -\ 6.53 \\ \hline 8.77 \end{array}$$

14.
$$\begin{array}{r} 2.64 \\ +8.41 \\ \hline 11.05 \end{array}$$

Practice: Copy and Solve Find the sum or difference.

15. $6.3 + 2.98 + 7.7$
16.98

16. $27.96 - 16.2$
11.76

17. $12.63 + 15.04$
27.67

18. $9.24 - 2.68$
6.56

19. $\$18 - \$3.55$
$14.45

20. $9.73 - 2.52$
7.21

21. $\$54.78 + \$43.62$
$98.40

22. $7.25 + 0.25 + 1.5$
9

23. $14.56 - 7.8$
6.76

24. $3.35 + 1.4 + 3.65$
8.4

25. $\$22.50 - \$8.99$
$13.51

26. $9.77 + 5.54$
15.31

H.O.T. Algebra Find the missing number.

27. $n - 9.02 = 3.85$

$n = \underline{\quad 12.87 \quad}$

28. $n + 31.53 = 62.4$

$n = \underline{\quad 30.87 \quad}$

29. $9.2 + n + 8.4 = 20.8$

$n = \underline{\quad 3.2 \quad}$

© Houghton Mifflin Harcourt Publishing Company

Chapter 3 • Lesson 12   153

Extend the Math   Activity

Investigate Students can use mental math and what they know about whole numbers to find decimal sums and differences.

Find 0.01 more than and 0.01 less than 7.35.

Think: When you add 0.01 to a decimal, you increase the digit in the hundredths place by 1. When you subtract 0.01, you decrease the digit in the hundredths place by 1.

- Which digit is in the hundredths place? 5
- What will the digit be when it is increased by 1? 6
- What will the digit be when it is decreased by 1? 4

So, $7.35 + 0.01 = 7.36$ and $7.35 - 0.01 = 7.34$.

Solve.

1. $15.39 + 0.1$ 15.49
2. $3.53 - 0.1$ 3.43
3. $0.88 + 0.01$ 0.89
4. $55.23 + 0.01$ 55.24
5. $9.68 - 0.01$ 9.67
6. $38.41 - 0.01$ 38.4, or 38.40

Summarize Students can use this knowledge to quickly solve problems involving an increase or decrease of one digit in a decimal value. Have students practice this skill by telling a story to go with the problem. Encourage students to use realistic problems, including money or measurements.

153   Chapter 3

Problem Solving

Use the table to solve 30–32.

2008 Men's Olympic Long Jump Results	
Medal	Distance (in meters)
Gold	8.34
Silver	8.24
Bronze	8.20

30. How much farther did the gold medal winner jump than the silver medal winner?

   0.10 meter

31. **Write Math** The fourth-place competitor's jump measured 8.19 meters. If his jump had been 0.10 meter greater, what medal would he have received? Explain how you solved the problem.

   Silver; Possible explanation: I added

   the 0.10 meter to his jump. His distance

   would have been 8.29 meters. This

   would have been enough to earn a

   silver medal.

32. In the 2004 Olympics, the gold medalist for the men's long jump had a jump of 8.59 meters. How much farther did the 2004 gold medalist jump compared to the 2008 gold medalist?

   0.25 meter

33. Jake cuts a length of 1.12 meters from a 3-meter board. How long is the board now?

   1.88 meters

34. ⭐ **Test Prep** In the long jump, Danny's first attempt was 5.47 meters. His second attempt was 5.63 meters. How much farther did Danny jump on his second attempt than on his first?

   Ⓐ 11.1 meters   Ⓒ 5.16 meters

   Ⓑ 10.1 meters   ● 0.16 meter

.... SHOW YOUR WORK ....

© Houghton Mifflin Harcourt Publishing

154 FOR MORE PRACTICE:
Standards Practice Book, pp. P75–P76

FOR EXTRA PRACTICE:
Standards Practice Book, p. P78

▶ ## Problem Solving *MATHEMATICAL PRACTICES*

For Exercise 30, why should you expect an answer that is close to zero? Possible answer: Subtraction is used to find the answer, and 8.34 meters and 8.24 meters represent nearly the same distance.

⭐ Test Prep Coach

Test Prep Coach helps teachers identify common errors that students can make.

In Exercise 34, if students selected:

A They added instead of subtracting.

B They added and regrouped incorrectly.

C They did not subtract the digits in the ones place.

4 SUMMARIZE *MATHEMATICAL PRACTICES*

Essential Question

Which method could you choose to find decimal sums and differences? Possible answer: I could choose to use mental math and properties, paper and pencil, or a calculator.

Math Journal

Write and solve a story problem for each method you can use to find decimal sums and differences.

Differentiated Instruction INDEPENDENT ACTIVITIES

Grab-and-Go!™
Differentiated Centers Kit

Activities
Decimal Display

Students complete purple Activity Card 5 by using 10 × 10 grids to model adding decimals.

Literature
Halfpipe

Students read about adding and subtracting decimals to rank snowboarders in a competition.

Games
Ride the Course

Students add or subtract decimals to move ahead on the course.

Digital Path

- 📺 Animated Math Models
- iT iTools
- 〽️ HMH Mega Math
- ⭐ Soar to Success Math
- 🏃 eStudent Edition

Lesson 3.12   154

Summative Assessment

Use the **Chapter Review/Test** to assess students' progress in Chapter 3.

You may want to review with students the essential question for the chapter.

Chapter Essential Question

How can you add and subtract decimals?

Ask the following to focus students' thinking:

- **What methods can you use to find decimal sums and differences?**

- **How does using place value help you add and subtract decimals?**

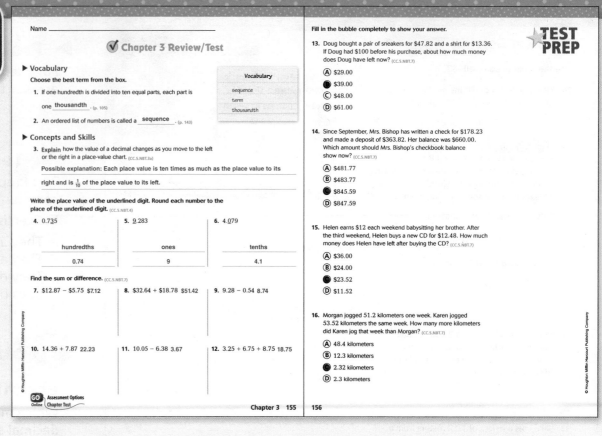

Name _____

✓ Chapter 3 Review/Test

▶ **Vocabulary**

Choose the best term from the box.

Vocabulary
sequence
term
thousandth

1. If one hundredth is divided into ten equal parts, each part is one **thousandth** . (p. 105)

2. An ordered list of numbers is called a **sequence** . (p. 143)

▶ **Concepts and Skills**

3. Explain how the value of a decimal changes as you move to the left or the right in a place-value chart. (CC.5.NBT.3a)

Possible explanation: Each place value is ten times as much as the place value to its right and is $\frac{1}{10}$ of the place value to its left.

Write the place value of the underlined digit. Round each number to the place of the underlined digit. (CC.5.NBT.4)

4. 0.7<u>3</u>5	5. <u>9</u>.283	6. 4.<u>0</u>79
hundredths	ones	tenths
0.74	9	4.1

Find the sum or difference. (CC.5.NBT.7)

7. $12.87 − $5.75 $7.12	8. $32.64 + $18.78 $51.42	9. 9.28 − 0.54 8.74
10. 14.36 + 7.87 22.23	11. 10.05 − 6.38 3.67	12. 3.25 + 6.75 + 8.75 18.75

GO Online Assessment Options Chapter Test

Chapter 3   155

Fill in the bubble completely to show your answer.

TEST PREP

13. Doug bought a pair of sneakers for $47.82 and a shirt for $13.36. If Doug had $100 before his purchase, about how much money does Doug have left now? (CC.5.NBT.7)
    - Ⓐ $29.00
    - ● $39.00
    - Ⓒ $48.00
    - Ⓓ $61.00

14. Since September, Mrs. Bishop has written a check for $178.23 and made a deposit of $363.82. Her balance was $660.00. Which amount should Mrs. Bishop's checkbook balance show now? (CC.5.NBT.7)
    - Ⓐ $481.77
    - Ⓑ $483.77
    - ● $845.59
    - Ⓓ $847.59

15. Helen earns $12 each weekend babysitting her brother. After the third weekend, Helen buys a new CD for $12.48. How much money does Helen have left after buying the CD? (CC.5.NBT.7)
    - Ⓐ $36.00
    - Ⓑ $24.00
    - ● $23.52
    - Ⓓ $11.52

16. Morgan jogged 51.2 kilometers one week. Karen jogged 53.52 kilometers the same week. How many more kilometers did Karen jog that week than Morgan? (CC.5.NBT.7)
    - Ⓐ 48.4 kilometers
    - Ⓑ 12.3 kilometers
    - ● 2.32 kilometers
    - Ⓓ 2.3 kilometers

156

Data-Driven Decision Making   ▲ RtI

Based on the results of the Chapter Review/Test use the following resources to review skills.

Item	Lesson	*CCSS	Common Error	Intervene With	Soar to Success Math
3	3.2	CC.5.NBT.3a	May multiply by 10 when moving right or divide by 10 when moving left	R—3.2; TE—p. 109B	4.27
4–6	3.4	CC.5.NBT.4	May identify the wrong place-value position	R—3.4; TE—p. 117B	25.23
7–12	3.8, 3.9	CC.5.NBT.7	May not align place values correctly	R—3.8, 3.9; TE—pp. 135B, 139B	21.37, 22.37
13–16	3.11, 3.12	CC.5.NBT.7	May use the incorrect operation when solving	R—3.11, 3.12; TE—pp. 147B, 151B	22.40, 61.04
17	3.5	CC.5.NBT.7	May not regroup tenths	R—3.5; TE—p. 121B	
18	3.4	CC.5.NBT.4	May not round to the correct place-value position	R—3.4; TE—p. 117B	25.23

*CCSS—Common Core State Standards   **Key: R**—Reteach Book; **TE**—RtI Activities

Name _____

TEST PREP

17. Angelo measured the amount of rain that fell on July 14th. His rain gauge recorded 1.54 centimeters. If 1.73 centimeters fell between July 1st and July 13th, which model shows the total amount of rain that fell from July 1st through July 14th? (CC.5.NBT.7)

(A)

(B)

(C)

(D)

18. The Ruby Throated Hummingbird has an average weight of just 4.253 grams. What is its average weight rounded to the nearest tenth? (CC.5.NBT.4)

(A) 4.3 grams
(B) 4.253 grams
(C) 4.25 grams
(D) 4.2 grams

Chapter 3   157

▶ **Constructed Response**

19. The Smiths are on a summer road trip. They travel 10.9 hours the first day, 8.6 hours the second day, and 12.4 hours the final day. About how many hours does the Smith family travel over the 3-day trip? (CC.5.NBT.7)

Possible estimate: about 32 hours

Explain how you found your answer.

Possible explanation: I used benchmarks to estimate each

amount and then added.

▶ **Performance Task** (CC.5.NBT.3b, CC.5.NBT.7)

20. The prices for different beverages and snacks at a snack stand in a park are shown in the table.

Park Snacks	
Item	Price
Fruit Juice	$0.89
Iced Tea	$1.29
Lemonade	$1.49
Pretzel	$2.50
Popcorn	$1.25

(A) Blair buys a pretzel and fruit juice. Jen buys popcorn and iced tea. Find the difference between the cost of the snacks Blair buys and the cost of the snacks Jen buys.

$0.85

(B) For which two beverages is the difference between the prices the greatest? What is the difference?

Fruit Juice and Lemonade; $0.60

(C) What if a frosty beverage was being added to the menu that would cost $0.20 more than the fruit juice? How much would the frosty beverage cost? Explain how you can determine the cost by using mental math.

$1.09; Possible explanation: I can count up 2 tenths from

0.89. One tenth from $0.89 to $0.99 and another tenth from

$0.99 to $1.09.

158

Constructed Response

Score students' responses with a 2-1-0 rubric (see *Assessment Guide*). A level 2 response would include:

For Problem 19, students should recognize that benchmarks can be used to estimate the sum of the three amounts.

Performance Indicators

A student with a level 3 paper

_____ identifies the information needed to solve the problem.

_____ correctly uses place value to add and subtract decimals.

_____ compares and orders decimals correctly.

_____ shows work and explains how answers were determined.

Performance Task

Use the performance indicators, scoring rubric, and DOK level to evaluate conceptual understanding.

Performance Assessment

Depth of Knowledge

Item	DOK Level
20A	2
20B	2
20C	3

Performance Assessment

Chapters 1–5

See *Assessment Guide* for Performance Tasks to be completed at the end of each critical area.

Performance Task Scoring Rubric

3	**Generally accurate, complete, and clear:** All parts of the task are successfully completed. The student demonstrates sound reasoning and an understanding of the key concepts and procedures. Explanations are complete and clear with no meaningful errors.
2	**Accurate results without sufficient support:** All parts of the task are completed. While correct answers may indicate some understanding of the key concepts and procedures, explanations are lacking in reasoning and mathematical justification.
1	**Partially accurate:** Part of the task is successfully completed while other parts may be attempted, but not successfully completed. The student demonstrates minimal understanding of key concepts and procedures.
0	**Not accurate, complete, and clear:** No part of the task is completed with any success. There is little, if any, evidence that the student understands key concepts and procedures.

Performance Task may be used for portfolios.

Chapter 3
Test

Summative Assessment

Use the **Chapter Test** to assess students' progress in Chapter 3.

Chapter Tests are provided in multiple-choice and mixed-response format in the *Assessment Guide*.

GO Online Chapter 3 Test is available online.

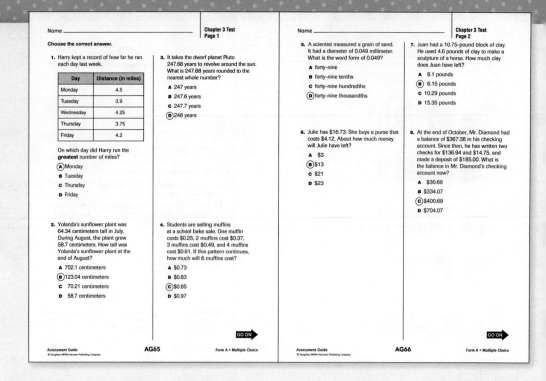

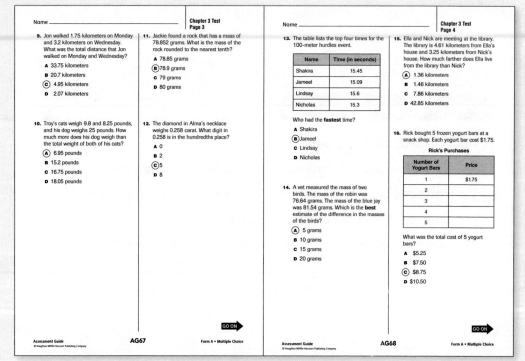

✓Data-Driven Decision Making 🔺RtI

Item	Lesson	*CCSS	Common Error	Intervene With	Soar to Success Math
1, 13, 24	3.3	CC.5.NBT.3b	May not understand how to compare and order decimals	R—3.3; TE—p. 113B	8.44
2, 9, 22	3.8	CC.5.NBT.7	May line up the decimal place values incorrectly before adding	R—3.8; TE—p. 135B	21.37
3, 11, 21	3.4	CC.5.NBT.4	May not understand how to round a decimal to a given place	R—3.4; TE—p. 117B	25.23
4, 18	3.10	CC.5.NBT.7	May not compute correctly to find a pattern	R—3.10; TE—p. 143B	27.24

***CCSS**—Common Core State Standards **Key: R**—Reteach Book; **TE**—RtI Activities

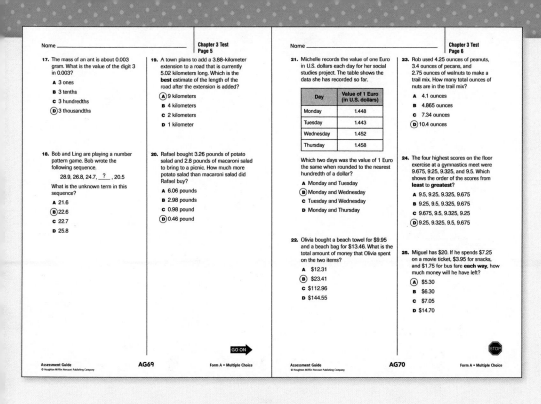

Name _____ Chapter 3 Test / Page 5

17. The mass of an ant is about 0.003 gram. What is the value of the digit 3 in 0.003?

A 3 ones
B 3 tenths
C 3 hundredths
(D) 3 thousandths

18. Bob and Ling are playing a number pattern game. Bob wrote the following sequence.

28.9, 26.8, 24.7, __?__ , 20.5

What is the unknown term in this sequence?

A 21.6
(B) 22.6
C 22.7
D 25.8

19. A town plans to add a 3.88-kilometer extension to a road that is currently 5.02 kilometers long. Which is the **best** estimate of the length of the road after the extension is added?

(A) 9 kilometers
B 4 kilometers
C 2 kilometers
D 1 kilometer

20. Rafael bought 3.26 pounds of potato salad and 2.8 pounds of macaroni salad to bring to a picnic. How much more potato salad than macaroni salad did Rafael buy?

A 6.06 pounds
B 2.98 pounds
C 0.98 pound
(D) 0.46 pound

Name _____ Chapter 3 Test / Page 6

21. Michelle records the value of one Euro in U.S. dollars each day for her social studies project. The table shows the data she has recorded so far.

Day	Value of 1 Euro (in U.S. dollars)
Monday	1.448
Tuesday	1.443
Wednesday	1.452
Thursday	1.458

Which two days was the value of 1 Euro the same when rounded to the nearest hundredth of a dollar?

A Monday and Tuesday
(B) Monday and Wednesday
C Tuesday and Wednesday
D Monday and Thursday

22. Olivia bought a beach towel for $9.95 and a beach bag for $13.46. What is the total amount of money that Olivia spent on the two items?

A $12.31
(B) $23.41
C $112.96
D $144.55

23. Rob used 4.25 ounces of peanuts, 3.4 ounces of pecans, and 2.75 ounces of walnuts to make a trail mix. How many total ounces of nuts are in the trail mix?

A 4.1 ounces
B 4.865 ounces
C 7.34 ounces
(D) 10.4 ounces

24. The four highest scores on the floor exercise at a gymnastics meet were 9.675, 9.25, 9.325, and 9.5. Which shows the order of the scores from **least** to **greatest**?

A 9.5, 9.25, 9.325, 9.675
B 9.25, 9.5, 9.325, 9.675
C 9.675, 9.5, 9.325, 9.25
(D) 9.25, 9.325, 9.5, 9.675

25. Miguel has $20. If he spends $7.25 on a movie ticket, $3.95 for snacks, and $1.75 for bus fare **each way**, how much money will he have left?

(A) $5.30
B $6.30
C $7.05
D $14.70

Assessment Guide — AG69 — Form A • Multiple Choice
© Houghton Mifflin Harcourt Publishing Company

Assessment Guide — AG70 — Form A • Multiple Choice
© Houghton Mifflin Harcourt Publishing Company

Portfolio Suggestions The portfolio represents the growth, talents, achievements, and reflections of the mathematics learner. Students might spend a short time selecting work samples for their portfolios and completing A Guide to My Math Portfolio from the *Assessment Guide*.

You many want to have students respond to the following questions:

- What new understanding of math have I developed in the past several weeks?
- What growth in understanding or skills can I see in my work?
- What can I do to improve my understanding of math ideas?
- What would I like to learn more about?

For information about how to organize, share, and evaluate portfolios, see the *Assessment Guide*.

Chapter 3 Test

✓ Data-Driven Decision Making

Item	Lesson	*CCSS	Common Error	Intervene With	Soar to Success Math
5, 12, 17	3.2	CC.5.NBT.3a	May not understand place value	R—3.2; **TE**—p. 109B	4.27
6, 14, 19	3.7	CC.5.NBT.7	May not understand how to estimate decimal sums and differences	R—3.7; **TE**—p. 131B	21.36, 22.36
7, 15, 20	3.9	CC.5.NBT.7	May line up the decimal place values incorrectly before subtracting	R—3.9; **TE**—p. 139B	22.37
8, 16, 25	3.11	CC.5.NBT.7	May not understand how to add and subtract money	R—3.11; **TE**—p. 147B	61.04
10, 23	3.12	CC.5.NBT.7	May not understand what method to choose to solve a problem involving decimals	R—3.12; **TE**—p. 151B	22.40

*CCSS—Common Core State Standards   **Key: R**—Reteach Book; **TE**—RtI Activities